The
SKS
Type Carbines

by
Duncan Long
Edited by Larry Combs

D1319143

Desert Publications
El Dorado, AR 71731-1751 U. S. A.

The SKS
Type 45 Carbines

© 1992 by Duncan Long

Published by Desert Publications
215 S. Washington Ave.
El Dorado, AR 71730
info@deltapress.com

15 14 13 12 11 10 9 8
ISBN: 0-87947-065-8
Printed in U. S. A.

Desert Publication is a division of
The DELTA GROUP, Ltd.
Direct all inquiries & orders to the above address.

All rights reserved. Except for use in a review, no portion of this book may be reproduced by any means known or unknown without the express written permission of the publisher.

Neither the author nor the publisher assumes any responsibility for the use or misuse of the information contained in this book. This material was compiled for educational and entertainment purposes and one should not construe that any other purpose is suggested.

Warning!!

The Publisher (Desert Publications) produces this book for informational and entertainment purposes and under no circumstances advises, encourages or approves of use of this material in any manner.

Acknowledgements

Thanks must go to the many manufacturers and importers who sent accessories, catalogs, and photos for the writing of this book. Navy Arms Company and Century International Arms were especially helpful with supplying sample SKS rifles for testing along with information about their models and accessories.

As has been the case with other of my books, several ammunition suppliers including Federal Cartridge Company, Olin/Winchester, Action Ammo, Remington, Black Hills Ammunition, and PMC have again generously supplied ammunition to test the firearms covered in this book.

A special thanks to the people at Delta Press for helping to get this book from the idea stage to an actual book (with a special nod toward W.R. "Gig" Giacona for his work in guiding the project and shaping the dog-eared drawings and manuscript into its final form).

And my usual thanks must go to Maggie, Kristen, and Nicholas for their assistance, participation, and patience while living with a "gun nut."

WARNING:

Technical data presented here, particularly technical data on ammunition and the use, adjustment, and alteration of firearms, inevitably reflects the author's individual beliefs and experiences with particular firearms, equipment, and components under specific circumstances which the reader can not duplicate exactly. The information in this book should therefore be used for guidance only and approached with great caution. Neither the author nor the publisher assumes any responsibility for the use or misuse of information contained in this book.

Table of Contents

CHAPTER 1

THE HISTORY of THE SKS

While it is not generally recognized as having done so, Russia was the first country to develop what would now be called an assault rifle. While the term "assault rifle" is hard to tack down, it is generally considered to be a lightweight rifle firing an intermediate cartridge between a pistol and bolt-action rifle cartridge in terms of size and power.

The idea that led to the assault rifle adopted by Russia occurred in 1916 when plans for a lightweight rifle were formulated by Vladimir Grigorevich Federov (whose last name is also sometimes spelled "Fyodora"). An arms designer and authority on current arms designs, Federov espoused the lightweight, self-loading rifle in his book, Avtomaticheskogo Oruzhie (Automatic Weapons), published in 1907, and in a later book, Evolyutsiya Strelkovogo Oruzhiya (Evolution of Small Arms), published in 1938. The first book was important because it noted the merits of such a weapon; the latter, because it was to influence the Soviet designers working on modern rifles including the SKS and AK-47.

It would be a mistake to think of Federov as merely a writer. He was also a machinist and created several semiautomatic conversions of the Russian military's Mosin-Nagant bolt-action rifle. While these conversions proved impractical, the design work he did undoubtedly laid the groundwork for his next major project, the development of working prototype automatic rifles.

The same year Avtomaticheskogo Oruzhie came into print, Federov and fellow firearms inventor Vasily Alekseyevich Degtyarev unveiled a self-loading rifle with a forward cycling barrel. This rifle suffered from functioning problems, possibly because it was designed for the powerful 7.62x54mmR cartridge used by the Russian military in its rifles. But the rifle did display merit and the military asked Federov to continue his work on the firearm.

By 1911, Federov had another working model that the Russian government again expressed interest in. After a brief interruption to his work during which he went to pre-war Germany to spy on ordnance operations there (a job that nearly ended in disaster for the inventor when he was forced to flee into Switzerland just ahead of the German counter-intelligence agents who were apparently on his tail), he returned to the Sestroretsk Weapons Factory to continue work on his rifle.

While the concept of a self-loading rifle for the infantry was hardly a ground-breaking concept even in the early years of World War I; since the automatic pistols and machine guns were already being fielded by both the Germans and Americans; the idea of using a low-powered rifle cartridge was. Most of the military designers were striving to adopt powerful bolt-action cartridges to semiauto designs.

This design leap was made by Federov sometime during 1916, finally taking his own advice which he'd given in Avtomaticheskogo Oruzhie. Realizing that the powerful 7.62x54mmR cartridge was too powerful, he started a search for a more suitable, less energetic cartridge. Federov's final choice of ammunition was the 6.5mm Meiji 30 Japanese cartridge; although weak compared to the more powerful ammunition employed by most other armies, this round was an ideal "intermediate round" and perfect for what the inventor had in mind. Federov modified the cartridge for better feeding in an auto-loading mechanism, creating 6.5x50.5mmSRS. This proved effective and was soon introduced in a modified rifle which he designated as the "Model 1916 Avtomat."

Generally known as the "Federov Avtomat," only limited numbers of the rifles were fabricated in 1916. These were issued to the 189th Izmail'skiy Regiment and saw battle during WWI when the Russians fought the Germans. (Some historians have even speculated that the Russian rifle might have influenced later German rifles during the decades that followed.)

As is often the case with creative individuals, Federov was an individualist—the worst thing to be

The "Federov Avtomat," was the first true "assault rifle" to see combat; issued to the 189th Izmail'skiy Regiment, it went into battle during the latter days of WWI.

during the time that Communist bureaucrats were taking over control of industrial production following the ouster of the Czar during the 1917 revolution. While in theory Federov espoused communism, in fact he often expressed "capitalist" ideas like the need to pay skilled machinists and designers more than common laborers on the assembly line; such ideas made him a marked man in a system where all workers were supposed to be equal. The inventor found himself jailed for a short time because of "radical" views and even when out of jail often found obstacles thrown in his way because of his convictions.

This resistance coupled with the lack of raw materials, shortage of skilled workers, inferior machinery, and decisions made by committees that didn't have the slightest idea of how to run a manufacturing operation, created an impossible situation. Even though the Avtomat was finally adopted by the Communist military, producing the rifles fast enough to meet the army's needs proved impossible. (With a team of engineers and over 100 workers on the assembly line, only 50 of the rifles were produced per month at peak production. During the six years the plant operated, only slightly more than 3,000 of the rifles were ever produced before the operation was discontinued.)

The Federov Avtomat also proved sensitive to dirt and abuse in the field, and due to the bureaucratic turpitude, improvements in the design were slow to impossible to make in the new production models. In 1925, communist leaders discontinued the manufacture of the Avtomat and launched a search for a new military rifle and—unfortunately for Russian designers—called for a return to the old 7.62x54mmR cartridge.

As one might imagine, the selection of the 7.62x54mmR almost guaranteed that no suitable rifle could be created according to the specifications put forth. Despite the difficulties of the 7.62x54mmR, a new infantry rifle designed by Sergei Gavrilovich Simonov was finally adopted as the "AVS36" (Avtomaticheskaya Vintovka Simonova obrazets, 1936).

Strapped with the 7.62x54mmR, Simonov's "AVS36" was doomed to prove unsatisfactory as a battle rifle.

Firearms inventor Simonov in many ways epitomized what the communist revolution in Russia was supposed to have been all about. Born in 1894 into an impoverished peasant family, he received only three years of formal education in his village school. He labored at menial jobs until he was sixteen when he became an apprentice to a blacksmith where he worked until age 21. He then went on to become a metal worker in a small machine plant.

Two years later Simonov became one of the machinists at the Korov factory that fabricated the Federov rifles. By 1922, the ambitious young machinist had advanced to a "Master Gunsmith" at the plant, and because of the skills he displayed, was sent to the Moskva Vysshete Teknicheskoye Uschilische (Moscow Higher Technical School). Here he studied mechanical engineering, graduating five years later to return to the Federov design bureau in Korov.

Becoming a member of the Soviet Communist Party, Simonov had time to work on designing firearms, drawing on earlier designs he had toyed with as early as 1922. One of these, a self-loading rifle with a gas system mounted on the right side of the barrel, was presented to the "Artillery Committee" in 1926, but it was rejected because of the width of the firearm and the complicated steps in field stripping it.

Simonov continued designing rifles and in 1931 submitted another model that became a major contender in the search for a new Soviet rifle, finally winning the trials to become adopted as the AVS36.

Even though it was the best design of the rifles submitted, the AVS36 was strapped with the antique 7.62x54mmR cartridge. Soon the firearm proved to be unsatisfactory, especially in extended automatic fire which caused the rifle to become fouled and malfunction while the soldier operating the weapon took a beating from the excessive recoil generated by the ammunition. The "People's Commissar of Defense" in charge of creating and fielding rifles was soon searching for a replacement. Only slightly more than 35,000 of the AVS36 rifles were manufactured.

The 1938 trials took place without any rifles being found that were suitable for adoption. A rifle submitted by F.V. Tokarev was chosen as a possibility, and the inventor started work redesigning it to overcome the deficiencies uncovered by the testing.

The second round of trials saw Tokarev's self-loading design alongside a new design submitted by Simonov as well as one by another firearms inventor, N.V. Rukavishnikov. As is often the case, the most mature design of the three weapons proved to be the most reliable; the Tokarev rifle was adopted in 1939 as the "SVT38" (Samozaryadnaya Vintovka Tokareva—"Self-loading Tokareva"—1938).

Simonov continued refining his design and, in what was apparently a political end run around the selecting committee, pulled some strings through his connections with theCommunist party to create one more series of rifle trials pitting his improved model against the Tokarev design. Unfortunately, while Simonov's design was improved, the models he fabricated were not nearly as well executed as Tokarev's SVT38. Test results proved inconclusive and, since Tokarev was well-liked by Joseph Stalin, his design was chosen over Simonov's.

In fact the rifle was far from perfect. With the Nazi soldiers threatening to overwhelm the Soviet fighters along Germany's Eastern Front, Stalin insisted that an automatic rifle was essential for troops in the field and the dictator didn't want to waste any more time with trials. So even though the Tokarev design wasn't perfect from many standpoints, the order was given to put it into production.

Those in charge of the SVT38 program were plagued with problems from the start. Tokarev apparently had handmade the models used in testing and there were no blueprints for the various parts. Getting these drawn up delayed production, thereby infuriating Stalin who let his anger be known to those in charge of the program. After delays piled up, Stalin finally insisted that the

SVT38 design be abandoned, and the Simonov adopted. One of the chief engineers, Boris L'vovich Vannikov, finally argued the dictator out of the idea, pointing out that retooling at such a late date would mean no rifles would be turned out from the plant for some time.

Finally Stalin agreed provided several cosmetic changes were made in the design (principally shortening its bayonet and lightening its weight). As designers furiously rushed to get the weapon into production, some of the smaller parts which were prone to breakage were strengthened and the stock was simplified as well; the "new and improved" model became known as the "SVT40."

Plagued with problems both in getting into production as well as on the battlefield, the SVT38/40 proved to be a poor combat weapon.

Once production was finally started, a lighter, short carbine variant was also created along with a scoped sniper rifle and an selective fire version (the AVT40). Unfortunately the rifle was still plagued with the cartridge it was saddled with, often failing to operate reliably in the field. But the severe needs of the Soviet military during World War II didn't allow time for any more changes in the rifles; production continued with over 1,326,000 of the standard SVT40 being manufactured from 1940 to 1942 along with 51,000 of the sniper versions. Following the war, the State Defense Committee proposed ceasing production of the SVT40, but Stalin nixed the proposal; possibly another 500,000 of the rifles were produced.

During the war the Soviets had had better luck with their submachine guns and it seems likely that these too, had a strong influence on subsequent rifle design. Up until the late 1930s, the USSR showed little enthusiasm for submachine guns with only token numbers of poorly designed weapons.

That changed during 1939 and 1940; the Winter War with Finland proved first hand to the Soviet Army what it was like to be on the receiving end of things when an enemy was armed with submachine guns and employed good tactics.

The Finns developed a strategy of using camouflage to hide troops in the forest; waiting to ambush Russian forces at close range. Here the long range but slow-firing bolt-action rifles the Soviet forces carried were at a distinct disadvantage when facing the withering fire delivered by nearby Finnish troops.

This defeat undoubtedly helped remove the PPD submachine gun developed by Degtyarev from its position in limbo to the forefront of the military weapons programs. The submachine gun borrowed heavily from the German MP28 and Finnish Suomi and was made of high quality parts and fed from a removable magazine. Capable of delivering the withering firepower used by the Finns, the only catch to the PPD was that it was expensive to manufacture with a number of machined parts and tight tolerances. In an effort to overcome this problem, the weapon was modified to become the PPD-

40, but it was still an expensive gun to make.

Following the early German victories during their invasion of the USSR in 1941, the Soviets retreated quickly in order to save their troops. In the haste to escape the Nazi invasion, large numbers of arms were left behind. The Soviets needed weapons and needed them quickly.

This push led to the adoption of a submachine gun design that was considerably easier to produce then the PPD-40. Designed by Georgi Shpagin , the submachine gun, designated the PPSh-41, was quick and easy to produce and functioned even when parts were roughly finished. Adding to its abilities to function reliably in the field was an easy field-stripping procedure that utilized a forward hinge on the receiver that allowed the bolt and barrel to be easily cleaned in the field.

The Soviet arms industry stamped out PPSh-41s like there was no tomorrow (which is probably just how it seemed with the Germans advancing toward the Russian heartland). By the war's end, over five million of the PPSh-41s were made and the Soviets often armed entire units with little else. Tactics that utilized the heavy firepower were developed; these undoubtedly had a great influence following the war on the development of subsequent infantry small arms used by the Soviets.

Because of the problems with wear and tear exhibited by the rifles fielded by the Soviets coupled with the success of the PPSh-41, military decision makers finally returned to Federov's original idea of using a reduced-power round in rifles, giving the weapon the ability to lay down a withering barrage of fire like a submachine gun while also obtaining the greater range that the submachine gun lacked due to the low velocity pistol cartridge it used.

It seems likely that Soviet planners had also been influenced in reaching this decision by the U. S. M1 Carbine and German assault rifles, all of which fired intermediate rounds and proved to be well liked by the troops who carried them. Apparently the rounds used in the German guns made the biggest impression, judging from the final specifications for the new Soviet cartridge.

During the 1930s, the Germans had experimented with small, selective-fire rifles chambered for several small cartridges. While the introduction of the new rifles onto the battlefield was slow, it's also possible that the Soviets learned of the German work through their spy network.

From 1940 through 1941 the cartridge that was finally adopted by the Germans as the "7.92x33 Kurz" was being perfected. This round was more or less a shortened version of the German's 7.92 Mauser, using the same diameter of bullet in a shortened bottle-necked brass cartridge.

By 1943, the first German assault rifle chambered for this cartridge was being fielded; this firearm was designated the "MP43" ("Maschinen Pistole 43"—Machine Pistol being the German term used to describe submachine guns). About this same time, very limited numbers of the German "Haenel Mkb42" ("Maschinenkarabiner" or "Machine Carbine" 1942) were also fielded; these latter guns had actually been used against the Soviets by the Germans as early as 1942.

Unlike the complicated rifles the Soviets had been trying to manufacture, the new German rifles were laid out more along the lines of submachine guns with shorter than usual rifle barrels and pistol grips; they allowed for quick manufacture with many of the parts formed of steel stampings that could be rapidly fabricated on relatively simple machinery with a minimum of machine operations. The guns were also simple to operate, field strip and repair, making them ideal on the battlefield as well.

By the end of the war, the Germans had perfected these guns in the form of the StG44 ("Sturmgewehr 44" literally "storming rifle 1944" or "assault rifle 1944") was created; while only a few of these guns were made, a number of them did fall into both American and Russian hands following the war and influenced designers in both the East and West and eventually served as the basis of Spain's CETME rifles and Heckler & Koch's G3 series of rifles and submachine guns.

While the exact amount of knowledge the Soviets had of the German programs when launching on the development of a new cartridge and rifle is unknown, it is certain that their experiences with full-powered rifles and submachine guns brought them to the conclusion that German designers had reached earlier: a smaller rifle cartridge would be more ideal for modern combat. Consequently, the specifications of the cartridge the Soviets created is amazingly similar to that of the Germans while both groups worked, in theory at least, in secret.

Soviet engineers developed several new cartridge designs for consideration with that of B.V. Semin and N.M. Elizarov finally being adopted in 1943. Like the German cartridge, the Soviet round had basically the same bullet utilized in their full-power rifle ammunition in front of a reduced powder charge in a shortened case. No doubt to the joy of rifle designers, the new round also lacked the rim of the older round making reliable stripping of the cartridge from its magazine less problematic. The new 7.62x39mm round was designated the "M43."

The cartridge was ideal for easy chambering and extraction in a semi- or automatic weapon and whose power was such that it would be effective within 300 meters (the normal maximum seen in actual ground combat). The round was mild enough to avoid beating up the mechanism of a rifle and remained controllable during full-auto fire. More powerful than the German assault rifle cartridge (the 7.92x33 Kurz), the M43 had a heavy bullet capable of bucking crosswinds and retained enough power to penetrate light armor or barricades within the normal ranges of engagement between ground troops. Additionally the bullet could obtain its velocity with a shorter barrel than had been seen on earlier Russian rifles.

With the adoption of the M43 cartridge, Soviet firearms designers started scrambling to create a rifle chambered for the round, even though it appeared doubtful that a new rifle would be put into production since the country's resources were being devoted to quickly producing the SVT40, poor though it was.

One of the inventors who created a firearm for the new cartridge was Simonov. Like many inventors before and since, Simonov drew from his earlier successful designs to create his new firearm.

It would be a mistake to think that Simonov had spent all his time working on a rifle to compete with the SVT40. During the period from 1938 to 1943, he created two successful firearms designs as well as a number of less notable ones.

Perhaps his best work during that time was the PTRS anti-tank rifle that had been created to help defeat German armored weapons. Competing against V.A. Degtyarev, Simonov created a powerful rifle that utilized a 14.5x114mm cartridge designed to defeat armor plating. Both Degtyarev and Simonov's guns proved effective; the bolt-action Degtyarev was adopted as the "PTRD" and the self-loading Simonov gun was designated the "PTRS."

Simonov's other notable design was a new rifle created to compete against his nemesis, Tokarev. The Simonov rifle, which was known as the "SKS41", utilized features of his PTRS along with features of a less successful carbine designed to use the 7.62x25mm pistol cartridge used in the Soviet submachine guns.

Though it never went into production, the 7.62x25mm submachine gun designed by Simonov shows many of the features that would be used in his SKS rifle.

The new SKS41 was considerably better than the gun he had submitted to compete with the SVT40 several years before, and it was simple and easily field stripped. Perhaps with an eye toward saving production costs of spare magazines for the rifle, the SKS41 used stripper clips to feed its fixed box through a guide at the top of the receiver. Two styles of fixed magazines were available for the firearm; one had a surprisingly low capacity of five rounds while the other contained ten.

Because of the disruption of the war, the SKS41 was never fully tested, let alone put into production. The weapon was a sound design and provided a ready weapon that could be rapidly adopted to the new cartridge to create a "new" rifle chambered for the M43.

In addition to rechambering his weapon for the new cartridge and modifying the size of its gas system and recoil springs for proper functioning, Simonov also improved the mechanism adopted from the SKS41 by upgrading the latching system of the bayonet, shifting the stripper clip guides from the receiver to the bolt carrier, and doing away with its muzzle brake (no longer essential with the reduced power of the round and an expensive part to machine). Except for these few simple changes, the SKS41 and the new rifle were identical.

The "new" Simonov rifle received high recommendations by the communist committees in charge of firearms production and despite the short supplies of materials, an unknown number of these weapons were actually built and sent to the troops battling the Germans along the Byelorussian front. The new Simonov rifle performed as well in the field as it did in tests and soon reports were coming in praising the effectiveness of the new rifle that experienced none of the shortcomings of the SVT40.

By the close of the war, the new rifle was seen as the ideal replacement for the SVT40 and received the designation of Samozaryadnyi Karabin sistemi

Except for the spike bayonet, this Chinese-made Navy Arms SKS is nearly identical to that designed by Simonov. *(Photo courtesy of Navy Arms Company.)*

Simonova, 1945 (Self-loading Carbine system, Simonov, 1945) or SKS45.

Unfortunately for Simonov, his design lacked two crucial features: selective fire and a detachable box magazine. While the Soviets were embracing the design that was far better than the previous SVT40, they forgot for a short time the lessons learned about the submachine gun and the advantages of its high rate of firepower—made possible by the very features the SKS45 lacked. Even as the SKS45 was rushed into production, it had design flaws that were soon to make it obsolete as military planners and tacticians pondered the lessons learned from the war.

As the SKS45 was coming off the production lines, a new rifle developed by an army officer named Mikhail Timofeyevich Kalashnikov was about to make the Simonov's design obsolete.

Kalashnikov's new rifle copied many of the features of the SKS45 including portions of the gas system, sights, and receiver cover. It had the two key features the SKS45 lacked: a detachable box magazine and a selective fire mechanism. In just two years the AK47 had been adopted by the Soviet military as a replacement for the short-lived Simonov rifle design. The new AK47 was quickly adopted by the communist satellite countries as well as the communists powers in Asia including Korea and China. In time, the AK47 was to become the most produced weapon in the world, rapidly eclipsing the SKS45.

One can only wonder if the story might not have been much different if the SKS45 had enjoyed

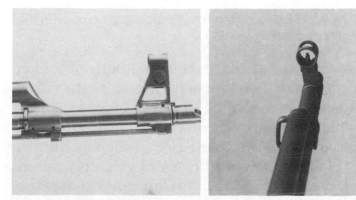

As can be seen here, the AK47's front sight (left) borrows from that of the SKS45 (right); in fact the sight posts of the two rifles are interchangeable.

The AK47's rear sight (left) also borrows from that of the SKS45 (right); note the stripper clip guide milled into the carrier of the SKS.

In time, the AK47 became the most produced weapon in the world, rapidly eclipsing the SKS.

selective fire and a box magazine; both of which might easily have been incorporated into the rifle's design, even as a retrofit. Doubly ironic is the fact that Simonov apparently created an experimental rifle based on his basic SKS45 design having a detachable magazine and a pistol grip and raised sighting system very similar in concept to that of the AK47.

Simonov created an experimental rifle based on his basic SKS45 design but having a detachable magazine, pistol grip and raised sighting system very similar in concept to that of the AK47. Unfortunately for the inventor, the experimental design was not adopted by the Soviet military.

History is filled with such what-ifs and there is of course no way to know the answer to this question—

which must have plagued Simonov even more than it does history buffs. Despite the SKS45's early demise, it remained the weapon carried by Soviet honor guards until the demise of the USSR late in 1991. And it seems likely that honor guards in Russia will continue to carry it for some time to come, reserving it a place of honor on the courts of protocol if not the fields of battle.

Backward-looking design or not, the SKS rifle proved deadly effective in the hands of communist fighters in Vietnam and elsewhere around the world where Soviet or Chinese versions of the SKS were shipped to rebel forces. Large numbers of the rifle were used by the Chinese as a "home guard" weapon. Later SKS rifles were exported to the U. S. and elsewhere and have found their way into the hands of many hunters who have discovered the M41 cartridge to be an effective hunting round when topped by modern expanding bullet. More than a few of these inexpensive rifles have been used for self defense or even target shooting, thanks to the inherent accuracy of both the rifle and the cartridge.

While the SKS has not enjoyed the success that its inventor might have hoped for, it has been far from a failure with the rifle achieving legendary status in terms of both reliability, inexpensive price tag, and accuracy. Few firearms designers could boast as much of their inventions.

Specifications for Soviet Rifles

Name	Barrel Length	Weight (Unloaded)	Length	Magazine Capacity
Federov Avtomat	20"	9.7 lbs.	40.9"	25
AVS36	24.7"	9.8 lbs.	49.6"	15
SVT38	24"	8.63 lbs.	48.1"	10
SVT40	24"	8.56 lbs.	48.3"	10
SKS45	20.47"	8.5 lbs.	40.2"	10
AK47	16.34"	9.56 lbs	34.25"	30

CHAPTER 2

VARIANTS of the SKS

Soon after its introduction in the USSR, the SKS45 design was adopted and manufactured by other communist countries. Among the most prolific of these was East Germany (producing the rifle as the "Selbstaqldekarbiner S" or "Karabiner-S"), Yugoslavia (as the "Poluautomatiska Puska M59/66"), and North Korea (as the "Type 63"). Large numbers were also manufactured by the Chinese as the "Type 56 Carbine" (not to be confused with the Chinese "Type 56 Rifle" which is a copy of the AK47); the Chinese version of the rifle is often exported as the "M21."

The Yugoslavian M59/66 differs from the standard SKS somewhat in the use of a gas tube shut off valve and barrel attachment for launching rifle grenades. This weapon is apparently aimed at the export market since it can only accommodate 22mm rifle grenades rather than the size used in most communist countries.

The M59/66 shut off valve on the right side of the barrel is engaged by turning it upward where it then doubles as a sight for the steeper ballistic arch of the

Apparently aimed at the export market, the Yugoslavian M59/66 differs from the standard SKS somewhat in the use of a gas tube shut off valve and barrel attachment for launching rifle grenades.

grenade. Special blank cartridges must be used for firing grenades and care must be exercised to avoid mixing standard and ballistic ammunition. In order to help tame the recoil generated by launching a grenade, the rifle is equipped with a rubber recoil pad. (Some of these models turned up in the hands of Iraqi troops in Kuwait during the 1991 Gulf War suggesting that the weapon has been exported to at least one Third World buyer.)

It appears the Chinese preferred the SKS over the AK47 and its spinoffs; when the time came to create a new military rifle, the gun selected bore more than a little resemblance to the SKS, combining features of the Simonov's rifle with that of the

When it became time to replace the AK47, the Chinese decided to adopt a rifle that more closely resembled the SKS. Shown here is the Type 68. Projection ahead of the gas tube allows adjustments of the port to accommodate a wider range of ammunition.

AK47 (most notably the rotary bolt and detachable magazine).

The new rifle, designated the Type 63, has a 20-round magazine with a bolt hold-open follower; most importantly, the mechanism is selective fire (with the control located ahead of the trigger). The Type 63 is made with both wooden and plastic stocks and it is thought that over six million were manufactured, principally for the People's Militia.

The Chinese Type 63 design was modified slightly to create the Type 68; the principle change seems to be a sheet metal receiver rather than the older and more expensive machined steel receiver. More improvements were incorporated into the design to create the Type 73 rifle and most recently the pattern has been modified further to offer a 3-round burst feature. This newest version is offered in both fixed stock configuration (as the "Type 81") and folding stock (as the Type 81-1).

The older SKS design is also alive and well in China in the form of the "Type 84", identical to the original except for a slight modification to the magazine well to accommodate AK47 magazines. While

Chinese Type 84 is simply an SKS modified to accept the AK47 magazine.

it may be that this design is principally for export, the rifles appear to be in use within China's borders as well. One innovation on the charging handle is the addition of a plunger which can be depressed to lock the bolt open making loading a 30-round magazine from stripper clips practical since the bolt can't clang shut when a clip is removed. (In the past, some of these bolts were found from time to time on SKS rifles imported by the Navy Arms Company.)

Chinese technicians have also helped at least one country, Bangladesh, set up a plant to manufacture the SKS (which apparently sold some of the guns it made to Pakistan); it seems likely that guns manufactured in such plants will see modifications in an attempt to capture a portion of the sporting markets in the U. S. or elsewhere.

Most of the versions of the SKS currently being made are direct copies of the original with the principle differences from the main design being one of very minor changes in the stock (usually only sling swivel placement) and bayonet design with the Chinese versions sporting the more effective spike bayonet (rather than the original spear blade). Because many of the parts of the Chinese rifles are manufactured by small contractors, Chinese guns also show a wider variety of finishes with some parts, including the receivers, seen in both milled and stamped steel variations from one factory to the next.

During the height of the Cold War, large numbers of the SKS rifles were exported, often as "political instruments" to help decide how a nation was governed when its population refused to adopt communism at the ballot box (as was the case nearly all the time). Later, the new government often replaced the SKS rifles with AK47s (or rifles modeled off the AK47); when this happened, the SKSs were often traded to third parties. Consequently "used" SKS rifles often turn up in unexpected places sometimes after being exported and resold several times.

Eastern Bloc SKS45s were exported to a number of countries including Afghanistan, Algeria, Angola, Bulgaria, Cape Verde, Chad, Comoros, Equatorial Guina, Guinea, Guinea-Bisseau, Guyana, Indoneasia, Iraq, Laos, Libya, Madagascar, Mozambique, Nicaragua (though used only for ceremonial purposes), Sao Tome et Princepe, Seychelles, Sierra Leone, Somalia, Sri Lanka, Sudan, Tanzania, Uganda, Vietnam, and North Yemen.

Soviet-made SKSs were exported to Albania, Angola, Benin, Cuba, Egypt, Grenada (by way of Cuba), Laos, and Vietnam. Chinese-made SKS Type 56s (and its spin-offs where noted) went to Albania, Comoros, Ethiopia, Kampuchea (Type 68), Laos, Madagascar (Type 56 Carbine and Type 68), Togo (Type 68), South Yemen, and Zimbabwe (Type 68). Additionally, terrorist groups were occasionally seen with SKS rifles from most of the above sources. (The PLO, for example, utilized SKSs which originated in the USSR, East Germany, China, and North Korea.)

With the apparent decline or collapse of communism in Europe as well as China, a mad scramble for Western money and technology has resulted; it seems likely that the SKS will remain important to these countries as they attempt to balance trade and import what they are unable to manufacture for themselves in the way of hi-tech equipment as well as the necessities that most of those living in Western nations take for granted. China especially seems to be going ahead at full tilt, churning out several versions of the SKS for the sporting market, many of which are exported to the U. S. Huge numbers of these Chinese rifles have gone to the U. S. and elsewhere with extremely low price tags making them ideal buys for those who have little money or desire a "knock about" rifle impervious to wear and tear that would turn expensive "sporters" into piles of junk.

For those in the U. S., Century International offers very low-priced standard SKS rifles with 20.5-inch barrels; these guns are hard to beat from either a quality or price standpoint.

Navy Arms Company is another good source of these rifles. In addition to the standard SKS models which it offers, Navy Arms has also created versions of the SKS which will appeal to some shooters and which aren't readily available elsewhere. Among these are the "Deluxe Sharpshooter" (marketed for a time as the "Farmer's Friend") with a Chinese Type

Navy Arms' **Chinese-made "Sharpshooter" with a 2.75x power scope and bipod.** *(Photo courtesy of Navy Arm's Company.)*

90 4x20mm compact scope and bipod; the "Sharp-shooter" with a 2.75x power scope and bipod; the "Cowboy's Companion" with a compact 16-inch barrel and no bayonet; and the "Para" with 16-inch barrel and bayonet. Additionally Navy Arms offers a rail mount that allows for quick mounting/removal of the Chinese Type 89 or BZM-1 scope which the company also imports into the U. S.

For a time, Navy Arms also offered an excellent folding stock for sportsmen wanting a more modern "pistol grip" on their SKS rifle (with the plastic stock

Navy Arms' standard Type 56 rifle shown here with the BZM-1 illuminated scope on the company's quick detach scope mount. *(Photo courtesy of Navy Arm's Company.)*

Navy Arms' "Cowboy's Companion" with a compact 16-inch barrel and no bayonet makes a very handy carbine. *(Photo courtesy of Navy Arm's Company.)*

Navy Arms' "Para" model with 16-inch barrel and bayonet. (Photo courtesy of Navy Arm's Company.)

having the added plus of making many SKS rifles slightly more accurate due to its tighter tolerances).

Unfortunately the U. S. government seems to have decided that looks are dangerous; even though an SKS equipped with a folding stock is no more suited for combat than the rifle with a standard stock, on Nov. 18, 1990 (apparently doing the usual last minute panic passage of laws by those in Congress intent on beating it home for the holidays) Federal Law Section 922 (r), Title 18 of the United States Code went into effect. Among other things, this ruled that SKS rifles equipped with the Chinese-made folding stocks couldn't be imported since they served no "sporting purpose." Even more ominous is the ruling that SKSs already in the U. S. couldn't be modified with a folding stock—whether the accessory was Chinese or American made. (All apparently because folding, pistol grip stocks made the SKS "look like the AK47.") Those looking for stories about the excesses of government bureaucrats should take note.)

The same type of thinking has also ruled out the import of the Chinese Type 84 rifle, even though (in theory at least) the U. S. Constitution upholds the rights of citizens in the U. S. to own firearms suited for combat (but not for sporting use—which is currently the only type of foreign-made firearm that BATF allows to be imported for commercial sales in the U.S). While the argument that the rights of U.S. citizens cannot be infringed upon by the government sounds good, the current ability of the government to trample the rights of citizens continues and the SKS in its detachable magazine and folding stock versions are not allowed to be imported into the U.S. at the time of this writing.

Stocks of the Chinese rifles that can be imported show a number of minor variations within otherwise identical designs and materials with a red fiberglass stock (designed for use in humid climates) sometimes seen in addition to the standard wooden stock. Trigger groups are often made of all-milled steel parts though stampings are often seen from time to time in various parts, especially the trigger guard. Whatever the material or method of fabrication, the variations all seem to be very reliable firearms.

Other variations are seen in the styles of bayonets on the SKS. In general the European guns have spear or blade bayonets with the Chinese guns having spike bayonets. However, perhaps in order to capture segments of the American collectors' market, some Chinese guns are seen with Soviet-style bayonets. All of these bayonets are attached to the barrel and can be released and locked in their forward or folded positions by pulling the knurled knob out of the locked position to allow the bayonet to be pivoted forward or back. (As noted in a later chapter, these bayonets are easily removed to lighten the rifle and give it a less militaristic appearance).

The cost of SKS rifles in the U.S. at the time of this

writing varies from $99 to $270 according to the condition, model, and overall configuration of the firearm. However, the prices vary widely according to the supply and the intense competition between American suppliers.

While the design of the SKS has remained stagnant for some time, it seems possible that the rifle might be modified to accommodate the popular .223 Remington/5.56mm NATO or other popular rounds just as the AK47 has. If this should happen, the end result would be a very inexpensive gun that would compete strongly with the more expensive .223 rifles currently selling like hotcakes in the U. S.

Even if such a new chambering doesn't materialize, it seems likely that the models listed in this chapter will supply the wide variety of needs of many individuals and governments worldwide for some time to come.

Chapter 3

Ammunition for the SKS

For a time it was nearly impossible to find quality 7.62x39mm cartridges in the U. S.; shooters had to make do with military surplus with corrosive primers. The popularity of the AK47 and SKS variants imported into the U. S. during the 1980s changed that; as more shooters purchased these firearms, ammunition manufacturers soon realized there was a growing market to tap into and soon all the major U. S. manufacturers and more than a few foreign ones, too, were offering ammunition in this chambering.

As the market grew, so did the types of ammunition. Soon not only could a buyer obtain bright shiny new FMJ (Full Metal Jacket) ammunition with bullets normally used by the military but also cartridges with expanding bullet styles. These latter rounds transformed the SKS into an ideal hunting weapon since the 7.62x39mm has about the same ballistics as the .30-30—an all-time winner at harvesting deer (but not ideal for use in a semiauto rifle due to its rimmed brass). Shooters can purchase a wide variety of quality ammunition for the SKS.

Some of the more successful military cartridges of the 20th Century. From left to right, the .223 Remington/5.56mm NATO, the 7.62x39mm M43, the 7.62mm NATO, the .30 Carbine, and the .30-06.

With this wide variety of ammunition, shooters can now carry on a wide variety of shooting with an SKS. Those interested in simply plinking will, of course, choose ammunition that is cheap and may even put up with outdated cartridges that are less than perfect. Those wanting to maximize the possibilities of their rifles will choose cartridges having expanding bullets, ideal for North American medium and large game animals as well as for self defense needs.

These hunting cartridges have bullets with SP (Soft Point) or HP (Hollow Point) noses which ex-

Today American shooters can purchase a wide variety of quality ammunition for the SKS. Shown here are four of the more popular offerings from Remington, Action Arms (Samson ammunition), Winchester, and Federal.)

pand in flesh to create maximum damage. They have the added benefit of not overpenetrating and are less apt to ricochet as well, making them somewhat safer to use (though shooters must always be aware of what is behind a target when firing any rifle).

For those reloading for the SKS45, it should be noted that most problems that result because of the ammunition in these gas-operated rifles are caused by too weak or too hot a powder load. Too weak a charge will cause the rifle to fail to chamber a new round, fail to cock the hammer, or—rarely except with very low powered squib loads—fail to extract the cartridge (remembering that these problems can also be caused by parts failures in the rifle as well).

Powder loads that are too "hot" will often cause the round to stick to the chamber wall so the bolt can't cycle back easily; such cartridges will occasion-

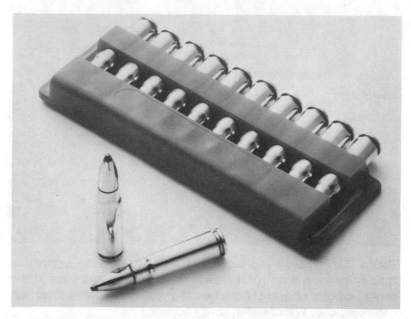

Close up of Federal's soft point hunting cartridge. These cartridges come in plastic containers that can be carried on a belt; the holders also make it easy to quickly insert the cartridges into an SKS stripper clip. *(Photo courtesy of Federal Cartridge Company.)*

ally even cause the extractor to break or cause it to rip the cartridge rim from the brass. Reloaders should also check fired brass for signs of excessive pressure; protruding primers, "melted" brass on the head of the cartridge, or ruptured cases; all are causes for alarm.

In theory reloaders will obtain the best results with bullets having the .310-inch diameter that matches the bore of the SKS. Most shooters find that the .308-size bullet designed for the popular .30-caliber U. S. cartridges work nearly as well. For those looking for the utmost in accuracy, Hornady offers a bullet designed just for the 7.62x39mm cartridge; this excellent 123-grain .310 bullet (#3140) has a soft-point tip and cannelures making it ideal for self-defense or hunting.

Good crimps on cartridges and cannelures on bullets are essential with ammunition in autoloaders, too. A crimp will help prevent a lot of failures to feed as well as minimizing the chance of damage to the firearm due to excessive pressures that can occur if a bullet is shoved into a cartridge during chambering. Good crimps also improve the accuracy of a rifle. Currently Lee offers a crimping tool that both improves accuracy and keeps the bullet in position during chambering; those who reload ammunition should invest in one of these inexpensive devices.

In addition to using crimps and cannelures on bullets, reloaders should also chamfer the outside rim of the mouth of reloaded brass to help prevent having the edge of the neck of a cartridge get "hung up" during chambering. Whether reloads or brand new commercial ammunition, a shooter is wise to test ammunition to be sure it chambers reliably in his rifle before going on a hunt or producing a rifle to defend himself. It's also good to remember that bullets with lead tips are sometimes prone to shearing during chambering so the rifle may need some extra cleaning in the chamber area from time to time if much of this type of ammunition is fired through it. (Damage to the tip of the cartridge has little effect on accuracy—unlike damage to the base which can cause a bullet to perform poorly).

Commercial ammunition that is ideal for hunting and self-defense has become widely available in the U. S. Among the best of these offerings are Federal's "76239B Hi-Shok" cartridge, Action Ammo's "762-25CL", Winchester's "X76239", PMC's PSP ammunition, and Remington's "R762391" all offer excellent cartridges with expanding bullets giving those using the 7.62x39mm for self-defense a large selection to choose from. For inexpensive practice, all the above suppliers offer quality FMJ ammunition.

Cheap military surplus ammunition is also offered on the market. Unfortunately, some of this still has corrosive primers which, though they won't harm the chromed bore of an SKS, can be very dirty and may promote rust on other internal parts of the rifle including the gas tube. Additionally some of this ammunition exhibits very poor quality control making it frustrating to fire and very inaccurate. Needless to say, such ammunition is generally best avoided.

The Warsaw Pact offered several variations on the standard M43 cartridge and some of these may eventually end up on the surplus market. Unfortunately communist manufacturers have generally used corrosive primers long after the West. So just as with the surplus ammunition currently on the market, the SKS should be carefully cleaned after firing these cartridges, too, since they increase the likelihood of rust.

Among the most common of the communist ammunition was the green-tipped "T45" tracer round; the tracer/incendiary "ZT" also marked with a red tip; the black-tipped-with-red-band armor-piercing/ incendiary "BZ" cartridge; a white tipped, plastic core practice round; a tracer practice round with a plastic core and a white tip with green band; a crimped blank (with the case extending into the area normally occupied by the bullet) marked with a rose tip; a shortened, crimped, and rose-tipped grenade launching cartridge; and various dummy/practice rounds with either a corrugated case, lathe turned black plastic, or nickel-plated/drilled case bodies to distinguish them from live ammunition.

Tracer cartridges are generally expensive and less accurate than standard ammunition; too, the necessity of firing a round to see where the rifle is aimed will quickly exhaust the limited SKS magazine. Often a laser can be employed more effectively at night for the same purpose, giving target acquisition without the expenditure of ammunition (more about lasers in Chapter 5).

Police and others using the 7.62x39mm cartridge have discovered that even the standard cartridge offers a lot of penetration with FMJ (Full-Metal Jackets) bullets giving even more. Some police departments have therefore adopted it as a "barricade breaker" for shooting through cars or other barriers a suspect may take refuge behind. It should be noted that this same excessive penetration makes it unsuitable for use indoors in highly populated areas, even when expanding bullets are employed—something those selecting this cartridge for self defense must keep in mind.

While the limited capacity of the 10-round magazine on the SKS gives it less firepower than most combat rifles have, there are a few "technological fixes" waiting in the wings which might one day change things. One of these is the multiple-bullet cartridge. These were first seen in brass cartridges in the hands of American hobbyists in the 1930s; later the Germans experimented with the concept during World War II and after the war U. S. military personnel continued the tradition. All these researchers found that it was possible to place two or even three small bullets in one cartridge, giving a shooter a "burst effect" with each pull of the trigger. The end result being a ten-round magazine of three-bullet cartridges in an SKS would be the equivalent in firepower to a rifle with a 30-round magazine firing three-round bursts of standard ammunition.

Currently such ammunition is not available commercially. Until that day arrives, the SKS45 performs most tasks just fine with its limited magazine. And a few owners enjoy detachable magazine versions that have no shortcomings at all.

Chapter 4

Accessories for the SKS

It's important to remember that accessories can't make a poor shooter into a good shooter nor do many of them do much to enhance the characteristics of the SKS. Some do help a good shooter maximize his abilities and some do make shooting a more enjoyable experience. The secret is to selectively shop and exercise some caution so only the accessories that are really needed are the ones purchased. Failure to do this will transform the inexpensive SKS into an expensive proposition.

Air Rifles

Most armies discover that training novices to shoot can be expensive—and it can be for citizens, too. Additionally, many areas of the world don't have readily accessible target ranges where a person can go and shoot a rifle; consequently, shooting an SKS can becomes an all-day outing with a long drive on either end.

Enter the air rifle. These guns are nothing like the BB guns many shooters grew up with. Modern air rifles create a heavy charge of compressed air that propels a small lead pellet up to 800 fps or more. This potent little pellet costs a negligible amount and the air (at least until Congress discovers a way to tax it) is free making owning one of these a cheap proposition. Additionally, because they are less powerful and quieter than even a .22 rifle, they can be fired even in many urban areas without disturbing anyone.

The catch is to find an air rifle similar enough to the SKS to make practicing on help hone shooting skills with the SKS. Fortunately the Chinese military has realized the value of training with air rifles and has created an SKS-style air rifle for training troops.

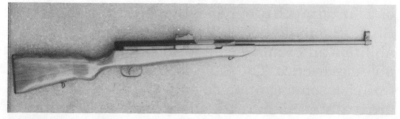

The TS45 rifle gives the shooter a lot of quality for his dollar. Created by the Chinese military for troop training, the gun is both accurate and powerful.

The rifle is marketed in the U. S. as "TS45" and carries a price tag of only $50.— a real bargain compared to most quality European and American air guns (thanks to less expensive labor and a plain-Jane stock of the Chinese gun). Available in the U. S. from Compasseco, Inc., this air rifle has the basic feel of the SKS45 and similar sights. With a weight of 6.75 pounds, it also has nearly the same handling characteristics of the SKS. As such, it is perfect for helping the shooter hone his skills on the rifle it's patterned after without a lot of expense.

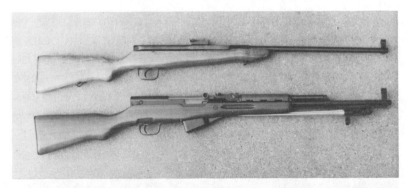

As can be seen here, the TS45 (top) is nearly identical in size and layout to the SKS45 (bottom). This makes it a good choice for SKS owners wanting to hone shooting skills with an air rifle.

Front sight of the TS45 gives a picture that is identical to that of the SKS and is adjusted in the same manner that the parent rifle is.

Despite its low cost, the TS45 is quite powerful as far as air rifles go with a muzzle velocity of around 800 fps with standard lead pellets. Consequently some care has to be taken to provide an adequate backstop for targets and protective glasses should be worn. Many owners of these air guns discover them to be quite accurate too; coupled with the power of the TS45, this makes it ideal for hunting small game or varminting at close ranges.

Since firing any spring-powered air rifle without

a pellet in it can damage the piston, care must always be taken to place ammunition into the rifle before firing it. And though steel BBs will chamber in the TS45, these are best avoided since they may damage the bore and their light weight makes them nearly as bad for the piston as firing the rifle empty. The heavy spring that powers the rifle may lose a little of its power if the rifle is left cocked for extended periods so it's best to fire shortly after cocking and loading the gun. Finally, shooters should be wary of the slight pinch hazard that can occur when the side-mounted cocking lever is snapped back into place; fingers must be out of the way to avoid a tweak.

For SKS owners wanting a fun shooting hobby that can be enjoyed anywhere from a basement shooting range to the "out back" of the back yard to the hunting of small varmints, the TS45 is just the ticket. The shooter gets a lot for his money with one of these pellet rifles.

Bayonets

Bayonets on any modern rifle are all but useless and the SKS is no exception. Even in combat, the bayonet is rarely used except, perhaps, for guarding prisoners. However, for those wishing to display an "authentic" SKS or planning on using the rifle in a re-enactment group, having a bayonet on the rifle will give it an authentic look.

Usually the SKS comes with its own bayonet, though some people may wish to exchange the blade or spike style for the other; in such a case a replacement blade will be the answer. These are available in either style from Gun Parts with the 12.5-inch spear-point blade selling for $27 and the 15-inch spike bayonet, for $23. Exchanging blades is simple: the front screw is removed and the blades exchanged (taking care to replace the locking spring from the old blade to the new one).

While more effective than the blade bayonet, even the spike bayonet found on many Chinese-made rifles is all but useless to most shooters.

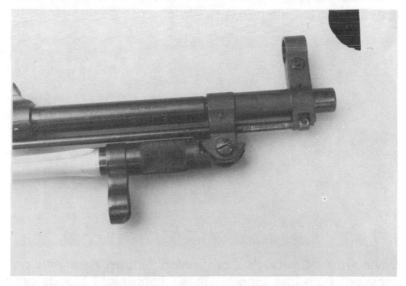

Exchanging bayonets is simple: just loosen the screw on the right side of the assembly to free the spring-loaded bayonet.

Bipods

Bipods aren't needed as often as many shooters think. Often terrain prevents their use. They can be useful in some target work, however, and urban police and military personnel in counter-sniper work might also benefit from a good bipod. Care must be taken not to add a bipod to the barrel of a rifle which may suffer from barrel flex. AR-15s, FN LARs, Heckler and Koch rifles, etc., all have potential problems with this even in their H-BAR versions.

Metal "clothes pin" bipods used by the U. S. Military are poorly made, often rust prone, and hard to carry when not in use. A better variation on the clothes pin design is available in Ram-Line's tough plastic "Universal" bipod which costs cnly $10 and can be quickly mounted or taken off the rifle. Made of a 66 per cent nylon/33 per cent glass fiber mixture, it is quite strong and the locking lugs on its feet make it practical to carry in a pocket.

Navy Arms' "Cowboy's Companion" shown here with an excellent Ram-Line bipod. These lightweight bipods are tough and easy to carry in a pocket. Their plastic lips keep the attachment from damaging the finish of the rifle.

The best permanently attachable bipod for most shooters is B-Square's "Ultimate" bipod that happily lives up to its name. Made of aluminum, these bipods are lightweight and have no exposed springs or levers; these latter features help minimize the capture of dirt or vegetation when the unit is on an SKS. The self-leveling, spring-loaded, locking legs can quickly be folded up or deployed and come in a choice of black finish or "stainless" models to suit a shooter's tastes.

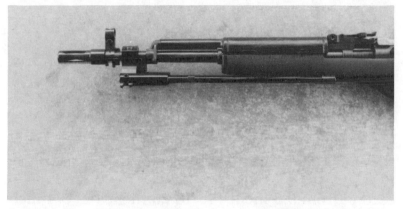

The B-Square "Ultimate" bipod, shown here with its legs folded.

The Ultimate can be attached to the SKS by simply tightening the two bolts on the bracket assembly of the bipods. This holds the bipod tightly in place. Since the Ultimate is made of aluminum, it adds only 8 ounces to the weight of the rifle.

Heavy steel Chinese bipods are also available from Gun Parts for $60 a set. While these will be too heavy for most shooters, those wanting a steady rest and a reduction of recoil may find this will be an aid. The bipods have individually adjustable legs that

The "Ultimate" bipod with legs extends. (The rifle is *Navy Arm's* "Cowboy's Companion" with a Choate stock assembly.)

extend from 9.5 inches to 13.25 inches in 3/4 inch increments and appear to have been originally designed for the RPD light machine gun version of the AK47; consequently they require that the bayonet be removed from an SKS before the bipod can be mounted (the bipods do, however, accommodate the cleaning rod).

Brass Catchers

Devices that catch brass when it spills out the ejection port can save a shooter having to search and pick up his empty cartridges after a day at the range. In addition to making it easier to keep ranges clean, brass catchers also help keep the brass clean—a big plus for reloaders.

E&L Manufacturing offers a rigid brass catcher that clips to the receiver of the SKS and traps empty brass inside it as the rifle is fired. While such an item wouldn't be a good idea for combat and can be noisy in the brush (where the plastic unit takes on drum-like qualities), it is ideal for target shooting or plinking. The E&L catcher rarely if ever causes a jam and holds up to 50 shells before it needs to be emptied. Cost is $30.

Flashlight Mounts

For those using an SKS for self defense, a powerful flashlight mounted on the firearm can be useful in some situations, especially at night. In addition to allowing targets to be identified so the shooter isn't firing blindly. And if the shooter is forced to fire, the gun-mounted flashlight will show approximately where the bullet will be impacting on the target since the beam of light acts as a rough aiming device.

The downside of having a flashlight on a rifle in combat is that the beacon makes a dandy target—care has to be exercised when using one of these on a firearm. Use of a momentary switch with the light gets away from many such problems since the flashlight can be rapidly switched on and off.

For added advantages, powerful flashlights with halogen or xenon bulbs can create enough light to dazzle an opponent. This can give a user of a firearm with a flashlight mounted to it an intimidating edge, especially indoors.

Most flashlights will accept a xenon or krypton bulb (available at most large electronics stores).

Bulbs should be matched to the type of batteries that work best with them and the manufacture's recommended voltage/amperage and specifications adhered to carefully. Matching the bulb to the correct batteries can boost the bulb and battery life by as much as 20 percent.

B-Square manufactures a "Mag Lite Saddle" which mounts a D-cell flashlight to most of the B-Square scope mounts. Cost is $20 for the saddle and mounting clamps (plus the cost of the B-Square scope mounts listed below). Flashlights designed specifically for mounting in 1-inch scope rings can be fastened to a standard Weaver mount on the SKS (more on these mounts in the scope section below).

A flashlight mounted on a gun must have a momentary switch so it can be quickly turned on and off. Such a switch also guarantees that the light will automatically shut off if the user drops the flashlight—or is downed by a shot. Having the light go off in such a case can be a life saver.

First choice of the flashlights available for use on the SKS is the compact "Tac Star" available from Adventurer's Outpost for $99. Its one-inch tube makes mounting it in scope rings a snap and a system for attaching it to the barrel of a gun is also sold. Although only 7.75 inches long and weighing only 9.1 ounces, the Tac Star puts out 20,000 candle power to brightly illuminate and dazzle an opponent. The flashlight also comes with a momentary light switch on a coiled cord; this can be attached on the handguard of the rifle to allow the user to flick the light on and off at will without changing the position of the rifle in his hands.

The Tac Star is built to last with a solid aluminum

body and rechargeable nicad batteries; a special recharging unit is marketed by Adventurer's Outpost to enable a user to recharge the flashlight by plugging into a car's cigarette lighter. The high quality of the Tac Star makes any other lighting system for a rifle second choice.

Flare Launcher

Arguably the ultimate accessory (and probably the least useful), a flare launcher modeled after the M203 grenade launcher (designed for the M16 rifle) is available for the SKS. SKS adaptor mounts are available; these place the flare launcher somewhat forward on the handguard so the unit hangs below the barrel, firmly attached to the gun.

These launchers are available from Tapco for $220 each. The units fire 37mm flares (running around $6 each). Since flare launchers are not legally classed as firearms, the launcher and its ammunition can be purchased without Federal restrictions by U. S. owners of the SKS (though some state or local restrictions may apply—those interested should check into these beforehand).

In theory these launchers might be converted to

Tapco's flare launcher is loosely based on the M203 launcher. While the practicality of such an accessory is dubious, many shooters find them a lot of fun and the units create more than a few stares at a rifle range.

fire 40mm grenades or the 37mm flares reloaded with explosives. Those capable of doing such conversions could likely make a launcher in 40mm from scratch. (And of course such conversions or construction is illegal without prior approval from BATF.) At any rate, such conversions to the larger caliber aren't practical mechanically or legally.

In short, this accessory is about as useful as dentures in a hen's mouth—but can also be a lot of fun for those interested in such gadgets. (For a detailed look at reloading these shells as well as how to improvise grenade launchers, see Ragnar Benson's "Homemade Grenade Launchers" available from Delta Press, Ltd.)

Flash Suppressors and Muzzle Brakes

Flash suppressors minimize the muzzle flash which can give away a position of a riflemen in combat; consequently most modern military and police rifles have flash hiders (also called a flash suppressors) attached to their muzzles. These devices don't completely eliminate muzzle flash, but they do reduce it, especially with ammunition designed for minimal flash and with rifles having longer barrels.

Muzzle brakes reduce felt recoil and make shooting an enjoyable experience where it was a bone-crunching experience, especially for larger shooters (whose body mass resists the rearward force of the firearm and makes felt recoil worse for them than for smaller shooters with less mass). The trade off for reduced recoil is added noise and flash, though some muzzle brakes do a pretty good job of keeping this to a minimum so the brake isn't too noisy.

A flash hider or muzzle brake has an added plus of protecting a barrel from dings and damage; this is important since damage to the muzzle can quickly ruin accuracy. Consequently, even sports shooters who don't need to reduce flash will discover that a flash hider or muzzle brake makes good sense on an SKS.

Gun Parts "M16-style" flash hider for the SKS. The unit slips on and is held in place by the tension of the cleaning rod.

A muzzle brake and AR-15-style flash hider are offered for the SKS by Gun Parts for $32.50 each. These simply slide onto the muzzle of the SKS and are then twisted to be held in place by the front sight and the spring action of the cleaning rod. (These units may require a bit of fitting on an occasional SKS with oversized diameter barrel but slip onto most guns.) The big plus of these units is that the shooter can slip them on and off as he needs them.

Gun Parts SKS muzzle brake helps reduce recoil and also directs gas upward to reduce dust problems during prone shooting in dry areas.

Laser Sights

Laser sights have limitations on a firearm but, thanks to modern electronics, these units have become both small and reasonably priced. For the uninitiated, lasers create a tight beam of red coherent light that appears as a bright red dot up to one or two hundred yards away in dim light. While this beam is straight and a ballistic arch curved, the two are close enough that a laser mounted parallel to a bore will coincide within several inches to the impact of a bullet over several hundred yards. This makes it practical to pin-point targets without using an SKS's sights.

The downside with a laser sight is that it's useful only in dim light. Sunlight erases the beam's red dot and, for those interested in self defense, and military users, the beam of a laser can be seen as a bright red light by anyone facing the muzzle of the firearm. Additionally, fog, rain, or smoke creates a beacon-like effect leading an onlooker directly back to the shooter. In darkness and indoors, the laser can be very ideal for some shooters, however, and for those who can operate within the parameters of a laser sight, it can be a very useful aiming device, especially when operated with a momentary switch left on only long enough to acquire a target and fire, then turn it off. Currently the prices for good lasers are from $200 to $350 each. Lasers have shelf lives of at least 10 years and their operational life is 10,000 or more hours if given proper care. Battery life varies from 30 minutes to several hours depending on the laser and whether it is flashed on and off or left on continuously (which is harder on the batteries).

Some lasers can be mounted in Weaver rings, within 1-inch scope rings, or on Adventurer's Outpost's flashlight barrel mounts (mentioned previously). B-Square also offers a "clamp" mount that couples their laser to a scope making it possible to have an optical system mounted to take over when the environment is too bright for a laser.

Like rifle scopes, laser sights have elevation and windage screws making zeroing simple (just use the iron sights or rifle scope and adjust the laser so it is in the center of the sight picture). Since most laser sights for firearms have a pressure switch on the end of a cord for activation with the thumb or fingers, care must also be taken to avoid snagging the cord.

Among the best laser sights available are B-Square's "BSL-1" and Aimpoint's "Laserdot" laser sights are good choices; both lasers fit Weaver-style scope bases or on an existing 1-inch scope.

Magazines and Stripper Clips

The SKS ten-round magazine can be very quickly reloaded with the stripper clips designed for it. These are available from a number of sources including SARCO, Gun Parts, and Navy Arms for a nominal price.

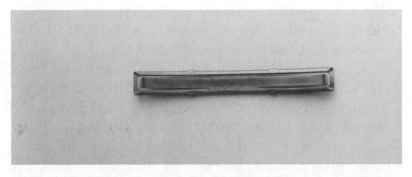

The SKS stripper clip will hold 10 rounds making it possible to quickly reload the magazine of a rifle by sticking the clip into the guide milled into the bolt carrier of the SKS and shoving the shells into place.

Since the SKS bolt locks back on its last shot and the clip guide is milled into the top of the firearm's bolt carrier, reloading from a clip is nearly as fast as exchanging magazines: Just place the strip in the guide and shove the cartridges downward into the fixed magazine; remove the empty clip and pull back and release the charging handle and the gun is ready to go. About the only drawback for some is the limited 10-round capacity of the clips and standard magazine.

For hunters in many areas, the 10-round capacity of the magazine is too great since laws may limit magazine capacity to 5 rounds. The quick fix for this situation is to use a small plastic spacer to limit the capacity of the standard magazine to 5 cartridges; these are available from K-Loc Mounts for very little and are easily placed in the magazine by releasing it before loading. K-Loc Mounts Company also markets a 5-round magazine for those wanting to permanently adapt their SKS to hunting requirements.

For a time detachable magazine kits holding 30 or more rounds were available in the U. S. for the SKS; but these were outlawed on Nov. 18, 1990 by Federal Law Section 922 (r), Title 18 of the United States Code (and while such a law is in itself unconstitutional and therefore illegal, notably so since the same laws don't apply to American-made rifles, those owning an SKS will want to abide by it unless they're interested in challenging it in court).

The law does have a "grandfather clause" that allows rifles converted BEFORE the law went into effect to continue to use magazines and parts purchased before the cut off date. (The trick is proving that the conversion was made before that date; those purchasing or owning such a rifle should be sure to keep receipts or other paperwork that proves the work was done before the date.)

Another joker in the deck is the size variations from one SKS to another. Some of the "detachable" magazine conversions that consist of a magazine with an extension on its forward edge are truly detachable from some guns while in tighter SKSs, the firearm must have the trigger group removed before the magazine can be taken out. According to a letter which BATF wrote (and which appeared in the American Firearms Industry magazine in August of 1991), written to owners of SKS rifles, "If you are planning to install a detachable magazine onto

Gun Parts detachable magazine conversion allows the shooter to quickly exchange magazines in a manner identical to many other rifles. Open cut in the side of the magazine makes it easy to tell with a glance how much ammunition is in it.

your SKS rifle, after this date [Nov. 18, 1990] you must install all magazines in a nondetachable configuration." So, according to this letter written by BATF, as long as a magazine is nondetachable (currently taken to mean removable from the rifle by simply pushing one lever to unlatch the magazine from the magazine well allowing it to drop or be pulled free of the firearm), any of the older magazines can be legally attached to an SKS rifle.

For those able to locate and purchase an SKS converted before the cut off date, three of the best detachable magazines are those offered by K-Loc Mounts, Inc., Gun Parts, and Golden Key-Futura (which sells a Chinese-made magazine). The Gun Parts unit required tapping a hole in the barrel to

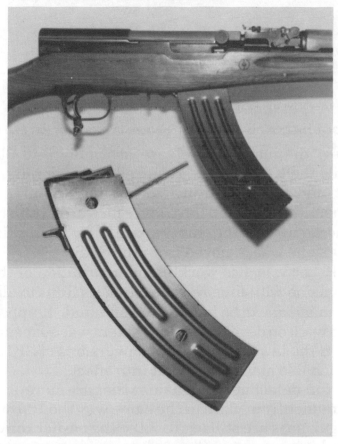

Golden Key-Futura's magazine holds 36 rounds. The forward plate is necessary to bridge the hole in the magazine well of the SKS. *(Photo courtesy of Golden Key-Futura.)*

K-*Loc's* magazine conversion shown in place on an SKS rifle.

screw the magazine release assembly into place while the K-Loc mount required no machining. K-Loc and Golden Futura magazines required no gunsmithing but did have large forward extensions to accommodate the empty space left when the fixed magazine was removed from the SKS.

K-Loc was also working on a variation of their magazine with fingerswells along its front to allow the magazine to be held by the off hand. It appears that work on developing this system was suspended when the law banning new conversions of SKS for detachable magazines went into effect.

Non-detachable magazines that are more or less permanently in place in the same way the 10-round magazine is are still legal. Like the earlier conversion kit magazines, these often need some careful fitting in order to function properly due to the variance in tolerances from one SKS to another.

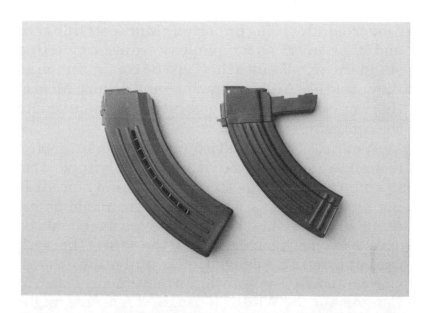

These magazines illustrate two methods of converting the SKS to "quick detach" form. The standard magazine on the left (from *Gun Parts*) requires modifying the magazine release of the SKS somewhat; these magazines are easy to carry in most ammunition pouches. The magazine on the right (from *K-Loc*) requires no gunsmithing work on the rifle but does take up extra space in a pouch due to the forward bridge section on the front of the magazine.

Tapco currently offers such a fixed 30-round magazine made of Zytel plastic for $14; it seems likely that other manufacturers will soon offer similar magazines. Chinese-made 20 round magazines for the SKS are also available from Tapco for $42; these are nearly identical in design to the 10-round magazine save for a larger capacity (and a star on the exterior of the magazine).

It appears that a few Chinese Type 84 rifles, designed to use the AK47 magazines, were imported into the U. S. before the 1990 ban against them went into effect (though these may have simply been guns converted after being imported); Midwest Ordnance and other American companies were also converting standard SKS45s into the Type 84 configuration so they could use AK47 magazines and drums. Most of this work was done to rifles which customers sent to the company.

While BATF officials (who wish to remain anonymous) have admitted that it is practically impossible to enforce this law as things now stand since it is impossible to prove when kits were made or assembled, those who own such conversions should be sure to keep any paperwork so the date of the work can be proven if challenged by the authorities; things change and if a strong anti-gun movement started in Congress or the White House, BATF agents might

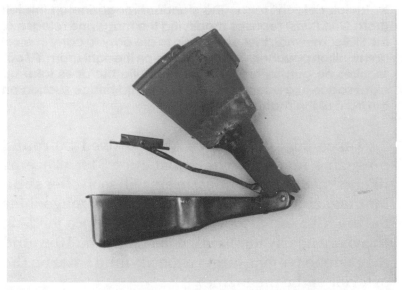

Standard fixed magazine on the SKS uses a spring-powered lifting arm rather than a magazine follower. This contraption proves to be most effective and is the most satisfactory magazine for most SKS shooters.

be encouraged to hassle owners or even confiscate their rifles if they couldn't prove the conversions of the firearms were legal. For those who can purchase such an SKS and the paperwork with it, these "Type 84" guns are especially ideal for delivering a massive amount of firepower—albeit semiauto only. In addition to the standard 30-round AK47 magazine, other magazines available for the AK47 will also fit the converted SKS rifles. Companies like SARCO offer Chinese-made drum magazines for the RPD machine gun (a beefed up AK47 design) having 75- and 90-round capacities with price tags in the $60-to $90 range.

Magazine Pouches and Carrying Bags

For those with an SKS that uses detachable magazines, the best bet for carrying spare magazines is to simply purchase a pouch designed for the AK47 or similar rifles. These are generally available at bargain prices.

Chinese-made chest pouches designed to carry SKS stripper clips are also sold by Navy Arms and others for $10 each. These are quite utilitarian in design and most American shooters prefer to have ammunition slung at belt level rather than across the chest.

The best solution is to go to a large gun store (or order through the mail from L.L. Baston) and check out the Uncle Mike's pouches and purchase some of these tough nylon assemblies to carry ammunition or magazines. The pouches match the other belt accessory carrying systems (including pouches for magazines, knives, compasses, etc.) that the company offers and mount on their excellent nylon belts.

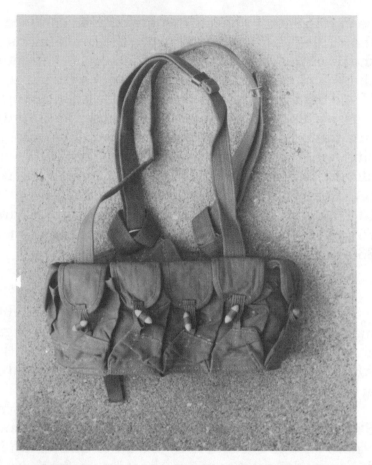

The Chinese-made ammunition pouch offered by *Navy Arms* and others is a bargain, though some shooters may prefer to wear ammunition somewhere other than over their chests.

Additionally, they come in SWAT black or camouflage patterns and wear forever, thanks to their Cordura nylon construction. Price tags are also very reasonable on these making them ideal for most shooters.

Uncle Mike's also offers excellent nylon gun cases with sizes to accommodate both the short "Cowboy"

Uncle Mike's also offers "saddle sheath" style rifle cases that fit the SKS. These are ideal for use on horseback or on modern motor vehicles. *(Photo courtesy of Michaels of Oregon.)*

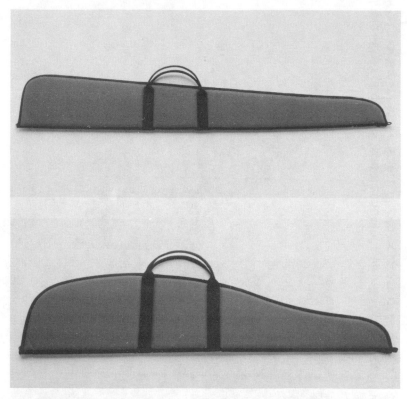

Uncle Mike's has a number of nylon gun cases that are ideal for storing or carrying SKS rifles. *(Photo courtesy of Michaels of Oregon.*

or "Para" model of the SKS45 as well as the standard rifle. Cost is $30.

Scopes

Given the inherent accuracy of many SKSs, shooters can often gain benefits from scopes on these guns. For a scope to work properly on any rifle, it must have a good mounting system—and the SKS is no exception to this rule. Luckily there are a number of excellent mounts that allow easily adding a scope to the rifle. Among these are three different models from B-Square; one requires drilling the receiver for mounting while the other two are somewhat bulkier but can be mounted without any gunsmithing; one model mounts on the receiver, the other on the gas tube of the SKS. Cost is $40 for the handguard mount and $60 for the receiver mounts.

Many shooters have discovered the gas tube mount to be very fast in acquiring the target when used with a small pistol scope or one of the dot scopes listed below. It is not, however, suitable for use with a high-power scope due to the short eye relief large rifle scopes normally have.

Another excellent mount is offered by K-Loc Mounts, Inc. This unit consists of two assemblies, one which is attached to the receiver (after drilling and tapping two holes) and the other which acts as the scope mount. The two pieces are held together by

B-Square's receiver mount shown here with a "compact" scope. *(Photo courtesy of B-Square Company.)*

B-Square's gas tube mount makes it possible to acquire targets very rapidly with a little practice. *(Photo courtesy of B-Square Company.)*

a large knob allowing shooters to quickly detach the scope for storage or when it isn't needed. Cost is $57.

S&K Manufacturing also offers two excellent scope mounts. Their 3465 unit (cost $68.40) requires no gunsmithing work to mount while their DT465 unit ($50) needs to have two screws drilled and tapped. Both units are very lightweight and compact.

Tapco offers a replacement receiver cover for SKS45s. This has Weaver-style scope rails attached to it. Provided the SKS45 has a very tight lockup between the receiver and replacement cover, this should work well though it may be slightly less accurate than some of the other systems listed here. Cost is $42.

For those wanting to mount the Chinese scopes offered by Navy Arms on their SKS45 rifles, the company also offers a scope rail that will accommodate either the Type 89 or BZM-1 scope. The unit goes on the left side of the receiver and requires drilling and tapping; once in place, scopes can rapidly be slipped on or off the rifle. Cost is $10.

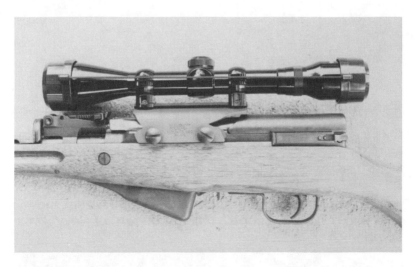

K-Loc's excellent detachable scope mount, shown with a 4x-power Tasco hunting scope.

There are huge numbers of scopes available to mount on the SKS45. Beeman, Tasco, Unertl, Armson, Redfield, Leupold, Simmons, Bushnell, Shepherd, etc., all have fine scopes which are tough and backed by excellent service and warranties. With the reasonable price tags on these scopes, it is wise to avoid little-known "bargain" scopes which are universally of low quality. (The only exception to this rule are brand-name models being liquidated by manufacturers.)

Variable scopes are best avoided on the SKS45 since these scopes can sometimes be plagued with frailties not found in fixed power optics and these become readily apparent with the abuse SKS45 rifles often get. A better bet is a scope in the 2x- to 4x-power range; this will generally be adequate for most users of the SKS45 which, due to its ballistic arch and power, is best reserved for shooting within a

Navy Arm's Chinese-made quick detach scope system, shown here with a Type 89 scope. *(Photo courtesy of Navy Arms Company.)*

hundred yards or so (though it is certainly capable of being used effectively at greater ranges).

For those interested in an "authentic" look with the SKS45, the Chinese made scopes designed for use with a side mount on the receiver are available in the U. S. from Navy Arms. The Type 89 scope is a compact assembly with a 2.75x-power optical system. As with other compact scopes, the field of view is about half that of larger scopes making it slightly slower in acquiring the target; this is not a major problem, however, given the low power of this scope. Cost is $100.

Also offered by Navy Arms is the longer BZM-1 4x-power military scope that is often found both on the Chinese military's SKS rifle as well as their medium machine gun. The unit has a battery powered illuminated reticula for low-light use. Like the Type 89, the BZM-1 has a throw lever on it that makes it possible to quickly attach or detach it to the rifle. Cost is $340.

Tasco has long been a favorite with many shooters since it couples quality Japanese-made optics with very competitive price tags. Among the Tasco scopes worth considering for the SKS are the "World Class" series, the "Compact" series (ideal for those wanting to keep their rifle light), "Electronic Reticle" scopes (for better shooting in low-light conditions), and the "MAG IV-44" series (with an extra wide view and greater light gathering abilities—also excellent for low-light conditions).

"Combat" scopes of abbreviated size have recently become popular with military users as well as sportsmen. These scopes are designed only for daytime use (due to their poor twilight factors) and have rather narrow fields of view, too. They are light and compact and therefore ideal for some applications. The Beeman SS-2, SS-2L, and SS-3 series are good choices in this category; cost ranges from $235 to $260.

Another optical aiming system that comes in sizes as small as the combat scopes are the "dot" scopes. Each of these creates a small red dot in the shooter's sight picture and has the added benefit of being capable of nighttime use. Dot scopes offer no magnification of the target but have a distinct advantage in that both eyes can be left open when using them. This gives the shooter a wider field of view making aiming quicker. Like regular optical scopes, the dot scopes are zeroed with one turret adjusting elevation while the other turret screw adjusts windage.

Two varieties of dot scopes are available. The easiest to maintain utilizes available light to create its dot during the day; some of these are useless in dim light while others use a radioactive tritium insert to give a green dot picture at night. The most successful of these is Armson's OEG (Occluded Eye Gunsight) available from L.L. Baston with a 1-inch tube for inserting into standard scope mounts; cost is $105.

The Armson scopes are only as bright as the light around them so firing at a brightly lit target from the shade creates problems for some shooters. Also, both eyes must be kept open with these scopes; those with some types of eye problems won't be able to use them(these people should go with the electric dot scopes listed below since they operate with one or both eyes open).

The tritium nighttime element in the Armson scopes will last for 10 years, gradually growing dimmer until it is extinguished. It can be returned to the factory for replacement elements for only a minor charge. The big plus is the OEG doesn't need batteries and is tougher than electric dot systems.

Electronic dot scopes use small batteries to power their L.E.D.s (Light-Emitting Diodes). These electronic elements create aiming dots through special optical systems. Since the shooter can actually see through one of these scopes they also give a better view of the target area. Prices vary from as low as $190 to as much as $430—and it's wise to shop around for the best price as this can vary greatly from dealer to dealer.

Batteries powering the unit must be switched on and off or it will eventually run down. But provided the shooter remembers to do this, they'll give hundreds of hours of use before it's time to change batteries—which are readily available at Radio Shack or similar stores carrying the hearing aid or watch batteries. Those using an electric dot scope in cold weather should invest in lithium batteries which will continue to function when regular batteries fail in temperature extremes.

Electric dot scopes can be used during the daytime or night (giving some carryover in shooting skills when switching from day to night conditions). Some scopes, like those from Aimpoint and Tasco also have 3-power optical attachments so the shooter can convert them into a long-range scope; Aimpoint also makes a 2x power red dot scope, fittingly named the "2 Power" for shooters who want a very compact unit with a small amount of magnification.

Another plus of electric dot scopes is that their brightness can be adjusted from a very dim point for night use to a brilliant ball for daytime shooting. Most electric dot scopes also have polarizing filters available for very bright daytime sunlight (this requires the use of both eyes since the view through the scope becomes limited).

The best electric dot scopes are Action Arms "Ultra-Dot"; Tasco's "Pro-Point" series; and Aimpoint's "3000" and "5000" series (available in black or stainless finishes and several sizes). All three manufacturers either have mounts that accommodate Weaver mounting bases or take 1-inch scope rings except for Aimpoint's 5000 series and all of Tasco's red dot scopes which have 30mm tubes (which are generally supplied with mounting rings for standard size Weaver mounts). Costs vary considerably from one dealer to the next but most of these scopes will carry a price tag in the $120 to $200 price range.

Slings

The SKS45 military sling is available from many sources for just a few dollars. These slings are adequate, but not as comfortable during extended carry as only slightly more expensive padded slings are. The best of these are those offered by Uncle Mike's as the "Ultra Sling." These tough Cordura nylon slings come in a choice of black, brown, camouflage, or "Trebark" camouflage and cost only $15 each. They're available at most gun stores or can be ordered directly from L.L. Baston.

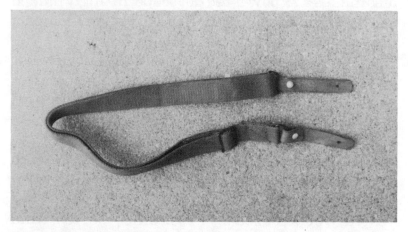

Chinese military slings are available in the U. S. for a song; but most shooters prefer something a bit more substantial when they purchase a sling.

Special Sights

Unfortunately, the SKS45's rear sight is not as quick to use or accurate as one might hope for. Yes, the bullet drop is (at least in theory) built into its adjustable sight; but the ranges the sight are calibrated to are greater than anyone normally shoots and the notch sight itself is not as quick as a peep sight.

One quick fix with this rear sight is to have a gunsmith solder a peep sight onto the rear sight blade after widening its notch. This will create a sight that is nearly as accurate as a scope, quick to use, and almost totally impervious to the elements.

The issue rear sights on the SKS are adjustable for elevation only; windage is done on the front sight, slowly, and normally with a special tool designed for the process. Additionally, the gun should be unloaded before messing with the front sight making such adjustments time consuming at best in the field. The solution most shooters employ with such sights is "Kentucky windage" (leading the target to compensate for the wind drift) and this works perfectly well in most circumstances.

However some target shooters may prefer a system that allows adjusting the sight for windage. Gun Parts offers a windage adjustable rear sight for just $15. The unit is easily installed and allows for the adjustment of both elevation and windage. (While the sight is still plagued with the notch system of the standard sight, a gunsmith can cure this problem by transforming it to a peep sight as outlined above.)

Colored front sight inserts are available for the SKS, though the standard black iron sights work very well for most shooters; Gun Parts offers a set of five posts (red, orange, yellow, white, and black) for $5.95 per set. This kit is ideal for those wanting to experiment with changes in the front sight.

Some shooters like the ring around the front sight and others loathe it. A quick solution is to cut off the top of the front ring, leaving two curved "ears" on either side of the sight post to protect it as well as give the shooter a method to lead a moving target. This work can be done by a gunsmith or a skilled handyman; touch up blue will suitably darken the cuts to the finish of the original when the job is done.

It should be noted that sights designed for the AK47 will generally fit the SKS; this may give the SKS owner a number of additional sights to choose from as more manufacturers take advantage of the growing popularity of these two rifles.

Currently night sights are not available for the SKS though it seems likely that these will be seen in the U.S. in the future. The best of these use a tritium insert in their front sight and—often—rear sight, too. Since tritium is a gas, it must be contained in a tiny glass vial embedded in the sight and under no circumstances should one of these tiny vials be fooled with: breaking it will release the radioactive material into the air. (If this should happen through accident, the area should be evacuated and windows opened to vent the gas.) It should be noted that the glass does contain one hundred percent of all radioactive emissions; as long as the glass vial is intact, the sight is as safe as most glow-in-the-dark wrist watches.

Meprolight and Armson both offer night sights for many other military-style rifles as well as popular semiauto pistols; these are available through L.L. Baston Company; price tags range from $30 to $150 (depending on the number of tritium inserts used). While it is possible a gunsmith might be able to adapt one of the sight assemblies available to the SKS, it is probably better to wait for a model designed for the rifle to become available from one of these companies.

Night sights utilizing L.E.D.s are also sometimes

encountered though none appear to be currently available for the SKS at the time of this writing. These units work well but require batteries to make their electronic element glow. Much the same effect can be created by using one of the red dot scopes listed above.

Adjustment tools for the front sight can be very helpful with the SKS sights. These small tools are available from Gun Parts for just $4.75 each.

Stocks and Stock Modifications

American shooters will often find the length of pull on the SKS too short for their liking. Consequently, many will be interested in replacing the stock or somehow lengthening its pull.

The simplest way to achieve this end it to place an E&L Manufacturing butt plate on a standard stock. The company sells an adjustable extension unit that mounts on the buttplate of the SKS to add anywhere from 1/2 inch to over an inch length of pull through the use of spacers included with the kit; cost is $25.

Gun Parts offers a rubber buttplate for the SKS for $15. The unit has a hole in its center to allow the cleaning kit's trap door to be accessed and mounts using the standard screws in the metal plate of the stock.

Those who shoot rifles in areas with temperature extremes often discover that the correct length of pull on a firearm in the summer changes radically when a heavy coat is worn in the winter. Then the stock's pull may be nearly an inch too long. The expensive solution is to buy a spare stock, using the standard length stock for winter and a stock with an extension pad permanently attached to it.

There is a very easy solution to the problem: the slip-on buttstock pad. These are inexpensive (less than $10) and available at most shooting supply stores; E&L manufacturing also offers an excellent slip on pad with inserts that allow the user to adjust the length of pull in small increments to suit his taste.

Another way to achieve this end is to place a pistol grip on the stock. This throws the position of the trigger hand forward, thereby lengthening the pull by about 3/4 of an inch. Gun Parts sells a pistol grip that attaches to the SKS standard stock for $24.95. The grip has a special hole allowing for field-stripping of the firearm without removing the grip and the base of the grip has a hinged floor plate creating a small storage compartment. It should be noted that the Gun Parts grip works only with milled receivers; the SKS rifles encountered with stamped receivers will not accommodate the unit without some extra work.

For the most comfortable hold with this pistol grip, shooters may wish to cut off part of the stock's original grip area to give clearance for the shooter's thumb and upper wrist when holding the new pistol grip (steps needed to refinish the stock are outlined in the previous chapter so alterations can be hidden when the stock is cut).

Firearms Specialties Manufacturing offers a pistol grip stock that is similar to the end result of using the Gun Parts grip and modifying the stock. Made of American hardwood, the Firearms Specialties' "SKS-47" stock is shaped for maximum comfort when holding the nylon grip that is mounted onto the stock. The stock has to be finished with stain, linseed

Gun Parts pistol grip for the SKS is easy to mount on rifles with milled trigger groups. The grip has the added advantage of increasing the length of pull by almost an inch for most shooters.

oil, or whatever finish the buyer wants and some slight fitting may be required to accommodate the stock to the wide variance in dimensions that is seen with the SKS rifles. Cost is $64.95.

A number of other aftermarket stocks are offered for the SKS including Walnut thumbhole stocks (from Federal Arms for $59) and Birch thumbhole

While it's possible to create a pistol grip by attaching an M16 grip to the SKS, the result isn't too comfortable due to the small clearance behind the grip. Too, this arrangement makes takedown of the trigger group a lengthy proposition since the grip has to be unscrewed. Best bet is to purchase one of *Gun Parts'* grips.

stocks (From Federal Arms for $40); these require some sanding and minor fitting.

Tapco offers a black Zytel Monte Carlo stock for the SKS. Though some shooters dislike the complicated lines of this style of stock, others find it very comfortable to shoot. Cost is $70 for the stock with a rubber recoil pad costing an additional $7.

Combat Exchange, Navy Arms, and others of-

Firearms Specialties Manufacturing's **SKS-47 features a nylon pistol grip on an American hardwood stock.**

fered a Chinese-made pistol grip folding stock (which was eventually outlawed by U. S. law); this plastic stock appears to have borrowed heavily from Choate Machine and Tools stocks (created for other firearms like the Mini-14) along with the locking system Ram-Line uses on its Mini-14 stocks. When BATF ruled that this stock served no sporting purpose (which has nothing to do with the Second Amendment but does seem to be the current justification for letting guns into the U. S. or banning their importation), laws passed by Congress went into effect making it illegal to mount the stock on guns already in the U. S.

To salvage investments in the stocks they'd al-

Tapco's **Monte Carlo stock transforms the SKS into a fancy hunting rifle.**

ready imported before the ban, several companies modified the assemblies by placing a pin into the hinge so it can't be folded. This creates a handy stock with a pistol grip and, for the time being at least, complies with the law. Those purchasing such a stock should be sure that the pin is well placed and can't be easily removed; having it come out would alter the firearm into a configuration that might cause legal headaches for the owner. Cost of these stocks is around $40 (these are also offered by Tapco).

Undoubtedly the best stock available for the SKS

The Chinese-made SKS folder was unfortunately banned from importation into the US unless it is pinned so the stock won't fold. Shooters should refrain from removing this pin since it would make the stock illegal to have mounted on an SKS.

is manufactured by Choate Machine & Tool. It combines classic lines with a comfortable layout; built of black DuPont Rynite SST-35, it is nearly indestructible and weather proof (and scratches are nearly invisible thanks to the texturing and material). The rubber recoil pad and one-inch swivels make this stock easy to carry and the most comfortable stock available when it comes to shooting the firearm.

Nearly as good as the feel of Choate's stock is its price—only $58, making the upgrading of a rifle a pretty inexpensive proposition. For those wanting a camouflaged finish, Choate offers a four color pattern for an additional $11.

Standard wooden and fiberglass stocks are often

Undoubtedly the best stock available for the SKS is the one offered by *Choate Machine & Tool*. The stock combines classic lines with a comfortable layout and is nearly indestructible and weather proof.

available from SARCO and Gun Parts for very low prices. These will have cosmetic problems in the form of scratches and dents but can be ideal for those wanting to experiment with bullpup configurations or who need to replace a cracked stock (the latter being a situation the author has never heard of with these tough rifles).

Experimenters may wish to try their hands at fabricating a bullpup version of the SKS using such surplus stocks. The bullpup is an ideal way to create a very compact firearm. The classic design is to use a double yoke running from the new forward trigger back along either side of the magazine, and then connect it to the original trigger. Some type of cover is then fabricated for the original trigger group and a pistol grip (with the AR-15 grips being readily

One possible configuration of a "bullpup" rifle created with a standard SKS.

available) used on the new, forward trigger position.

Those into electronics can create an electronic trigger using a solenoid to engage the trigger. A gas tube scope mount from B-Square (described above) would then complete the bullpup system with any of a variety sighting systems or even a laser. For maximum safety, care should be taken to fire only new, quality ammunition and the SKS must function perfectly. Any problems with firing such as premature ignition could cause a grave injury to the shooter since his face is so close to the receiver with this design. Of course a left hand hold is not allowed due to the ejection port and reciprocating charging handle.

Trigger Actuator

Amazingly inventive activities are often inspired by government restrictions. Such is the case with the current ban on manufacturing automatic weapons as well as intense restrictions on ownership of such firearms in the U. S. Yankee inventors have devised hand-cranked gadgets, trigger group inserts, and other devices that make rapid fire possible without actually converting the firearm itself to what is considered from a legal standpoint as a selective-fire configuration.

The most successful of these is available from Hell-Fire systems—and the company markets a unit that fits the SKS. The device attaches to the trigger guard of the SKS where a spring mechanism reduces the pull on the trigger. Placing the hand alongside the firearm and touching the Hell-Fire lever extending from the trigger guard causes the firearm to discharge very easily.

Once the user becomes familiar with the system, the trigger finger can be held more or less stationary while the gun recoils, the shooter's stance propelling it forward after recoil. At this point the lever touching the trigger is again tripped by the shooter's finger, firing the weapon. Each cycle of the firearm will continue to fire another shot, thus creating the effect of automatic fire even thought the SKS is shooting with a semiauto action. The end result is what looks and sounds like automatic fire, even though technically the firearm is configured in semiauto-only operation.

Needless to say, the Hell-Fire unit is fun to play with. It can also be dangerous if the user is unfamiliar with it. So for safety's sake, it's wise to practice with only a few cartridges in the chamber at first until the shooter learns to control the recoil. The chamber of the rifle is best left empty until just before firing given the "hair trigger" configuration of the trip lever on this system.

Anti-gunners might think that this device creates a dangerous weapon and some Third World countries have purchased these units for use with their armies. Nevertheless, it is doubtful that this would be suitable in combat where the adrenaline is pumping and the tendency is to clutch a firearm rather than hold it loosely with the finger poised to one side of it as is required for it to function properly. So it is probably less than ideal for most combat.

Nevertheless, the Hell-fire can be a lot of fun and, for those who have been denied the joys of firing an automatic weapon, its $30 price tag can give a lot of amusement for very little money (though ammunition costs can quickly mount up).

●●●●●

In addition to the accessories listed above, more are constantly being introduced for the SKS as it grows in popularity with U. S. shooters. One good way to keep abreast with the new products as they become available is to check the ads in Shotgun News. At the same time, shooters are wise to get the SKS into the configuration that seems right to them and then quit adding accessories or modifying the rifle. Overdoing things can be expensive and the end result is an over-laden firearm that is gadget heavy and often not much fun to shoot.

CHAPTER 5

SKS CARE, MAINTENANCE AND Modifications

There are many modifications that can make an SKS better suit its owner. The simplest of these is to buy a few of the more useful accessories (outlined in the previous chapter) and bolt them onto the rifle. There are also a few simple alterations that will make the rifle much more ideal for the shooter and most of these can be tackled by a skilled do-it-yourselfer.

Sometimes less is better. This is the case with the SKS's bayonet. Most shooters (including soldiers) rarely use a bayonet on a rifle; removing this assembly from an SKS rifle can lighten it by three quarters of a pound or more. Removing the cleaning rod and cleaning kit (which reside under the barrel and inside the butt trap) reduces the weight by another pound; even if a shooter wants to carry this gear with him, he's better off purchasing a new screw-together cleaning rod and carrying the kit on his belt where the weight will go unnoticed—which is not the case when it's on the rifle. Removing the bayonet and cleaning equipment will give the shooter a rifle that is a pound lighter and considerably easier to carry in the field.

The bayonet on these guns is easily removed by

simply unscrewing the bolt that retains it under the barrel. For permanent removal, shooters may wish to employ a hacksaw to cut the lower "dog ears" of the bayonet mount, perhaps leaving the upper half of the mount in place to retain the cleaning rod (or also removing it if the rod won't be carried with the rifle).

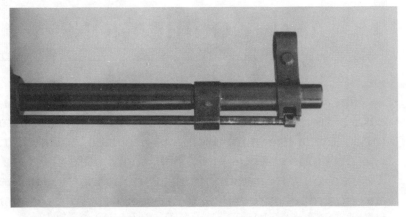

After the bayonet was removed from this rifle (from the assembly just behind the front sight), use of a hacksaw, file, and touch up blue finished the job giving the rifle a real "sporter" appearance.

A file can be utilized to smooth the surface of the hacksaw cut, matching the somewhat rough texture of most rifles as closely as possible. The bare metal can then be colored to the finish of the rest of the rifle with touch up blue (available in most gun stores or through the mail from Brownell's).

Removing the bayonet, its pivot assembly, and the cleaning rod and kit are worth considering since they reduce the rifle's weight by a full pound, transforming it from a burdensome firearm into a comfortable, handy gun. Additional weight savings can be realized with the purchase of one of the 16-1/2-inch barrel models offered by Navy Arms.

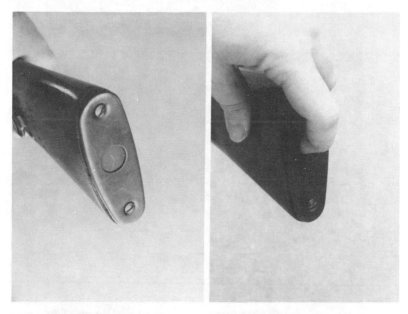

The cleaning kit is often stored inside the trap door on the butt of the stock. This should never be accessed with a finger (as shown here); doing so can trap the shooter's finger in the spring loaded assembly. A safer bet is to push the door open with a tool or cartridge.

Shooters should not be tempted to exchange parts between SKS rifles; some of these parts aren't interchangeable from one gun to the next, even in the same lots of guns which will have been assembled by hand, often with different individuals altering the parts to fit each other. Shooters should be especially careful not to exchange parts having serial numbers including the stock, bolt carrier, and receiver.

Those replacing trigger groups should approach this task cautiously and determine that the rifle will

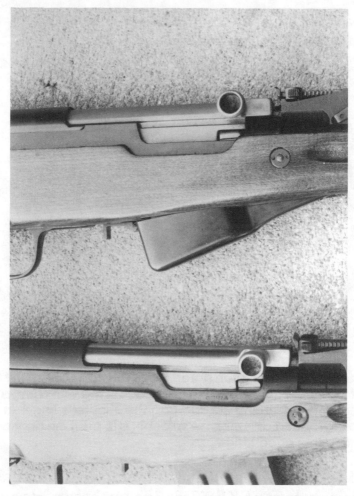

Notice the difference on these bolt carriers and stocks. The upper rifle also has a milled trigger group while the lower rifle has a stamped steel trigger guard and extended magazine.

function properly with the new parts, being especially wary of safety failures, hair-trigger situations, or other potential problems. Most such exchanges should be double-checked by a competent gunsmith to be sure the SKS remains safe.

As can be seen here, the stock on many SKS rifles has a serial number; this should match the numbers on the receiver. Note side mounted sling swivel.

That said, SKS parts are incredibly inexpensive. Concorde Arms is one excellent source of such parts, with companies like SARCO and Gun Parts often having a selection of various components. Past Concorde catalogs, for example, have offered SKS bolt carriers for $5.75 and bolts for $5.50.

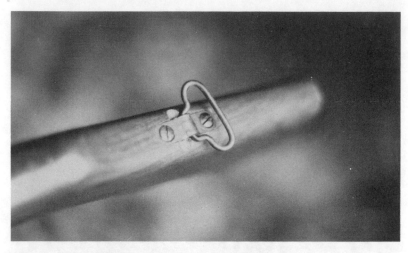

Small variations in the "furniture" of SKS rifles exist; unlike the gun on the previous page, this rifle stock has the swivel along the lower edge of the stock.

Accurizing the SKS

Most SKS rifles are capable of driving tacks and some shoot this way right out of the box. Others are less precise shooters but have the potential of being every bit as accurate. The accuracy of this latter group can be enhanced by attaining a tight stock-to-receiver fit.

One quick way to accomplish this is to purchase a quality aftermarket stock like those offered by Choate Machine and Tool (see the following chapter for more about these stocks). Another less costly but more time-consuming way is to "bed" the action with fiberglass. Either method will often shrink the potential size of groups to two inches or even one at 100 yards with quality ammunition.

Bedding the action must be done carefully since the material used (epoxy) is a very powerful adhesive. So it's important that any part that may touch the bedding material is coated with a release agent or the rifle may be ruined. (Bedding is a lot of work, those considering it should first shoot their rifle to be sure it is necessary. Often SKSs have tight stock-to-receiver fits that make this work unnecessary.)

While it's possible to use standard epoxy glue purchased at a hardware store, the best results can be obtained with Brownell's "Acraglas" kit (sold for $8). This comes with a dye so the glue can be colored as its being mixed to match the finish on the stock. The kit also comes with a release agent to prevent the glue from sticking to the metal parts of the SKS. For best results, the directions that come with the kit should be followed exactly.

For the best accuracy, the following spots should be coated with epoxy: 1) The top of the stock area toward the rear "U" cut where the receiver rests on the stock, 2) the inner sides where the receiver rests on the stock around the reinforcement points, 3) the top edge of the stock where the receiver on either side of the bolt rests, 4) the section where the rear of the trigger group rests, and 5) the edge of the stock that touches the receiver around the magazine.

Once the liquid epoxy is in the above locations, the rifle should be carefully reassembled and the glue allowed to harden. The latching mechanism on the trigger is not fastened tightly during this assembly; rather a little clearance—1/4 to 1/8 inch—is left between it and its locked position (this insures a very tight fit after the epoxy dries).

It is wise to remove excess glass compound displaced by the reassembly of the action before it hardens along with drips or "overruns." A small knife or other tool is ideal for this purpose and a cloth moistened in acetone will remove smears of epoxy.

The action of the rifle may stick to the epoxy after it has hardened. If this happens (and the parts have been coated with release agent), a gentle tap with a rubber mallet will free them after removal of the trigger group.

The bedding should be examined after the action has been removed to ascertain that the compound shows definite impressions of all the metal parts coming contacting it. Areas with large voids are sanded and more epoxy added along with new release agent on metal parts and the action rebedded. Once the bedding is complete, the metal of the receiver, trigger group, and inside of the stock are carefully examined and any excess epoxy that has oozed away and hardened in areas where it doesn't belong removed with a very sharp knife or rasp.

The end result should be a super-accurate rifle suitable for many hunting requirements or even target shooting.

Adjusting Trigger Pulls

Light, crisp trigger pulls generally enable shooters to obtain the best accuracy with a rifle. Unfortunately most SKSs come out of the box with horrible trigger action, often in the 6 to 8 pound range, usually with noticeable "snags" in the pull as the trigger travels through its long arch.

This can be improved with careful polishing and modification but such work should be left to a qualified gunsmith since it can result in a dangerous situation if improperly executed. One good way of getting this work done is to contact K-Loc. The company has gunsmiths who can tune the trigger assembly to a smooth 3-pound pull and get it back to the shooter in just a few days. Cost for this work is $86.50.

Often local gunsmiths can also do this work, though it may or may not be as good as the job offered by K-Loc (depending on the skills of the gunsmith). Such work entails careful stoning and smoothing of all moving parts including the top of the trigger bar (where the trigger spring may catch ever so slightly). Very careful smoothing of the sear and hammer contact points and a very gentle rounding of the sear will complete the job. Again, this is not a job for an amateur and a botched job can ruin the trigger group or create a very dangerous situation.

Field Stripping

Field stripping the SKS is fairly simple. In theory it can be done with just a bullet tip and bare hands. In practice, a drift punch and rubber mallet are often a big help in releasing tight trigger group latches and a tap with a rubber mallet on the top of the trigger guard is often necessary to latch the trigger group following reassembly.

The following steps will carry out field stripping:

1) The magazine should be emptied and then the action cycled to check that the magazine and chamber are both empty; the follower is then depressed or the magazine unlatched to close the bolt. The safety is then placed in its "safe" position.

2) To remove the cover and bolt carrier assembly, the takedown latch on the right rear of the receiver must be wriggled out, moving it from left to right; this will allow the cover to be slid off the rear of the

receiver. The recoil spring and its guide can then be pulled from the rear of the receiver along with the bolt carrier and bolt, giving access to the barrel and bolt carrier/bolt for most cleaning chores.

3) To remove the trigger group, the safety must be pushed forward and up (on safe). Then the small nub at the base of the rear of the trigger guard can be depressed with a tool to free the trigger group.

The takedown latch for the receiver cover is located on the upper left of the receiver. The latch is wriggled toward the right to release the receiver cover which is then lifted up and back.

4) Releasing the trigger group will also free the barrel and receiver which can be removed from the stock.

5) The gas piston assembly can be freed by rotating the lever (at the left of the rear sight) upward and lifting on the upper handguard; care

The bolt carrier and the bolt are easily removed once the recoil spring and guide are out of the receiver.

Safety (just behind the trigger and inside the trigger guard) in its "fire" position.

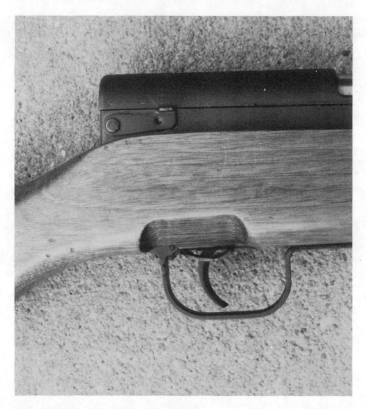

Safety rotated upward into its "safe" position, making the trigger assembly ready for removal.

should be taken as the gas piston extension and its spring are under pressure in the space under the rear sight; they can go shooting out unexpectedly if not restrained. The handguard, gas tube, and piston can be removed by lifting them upward and pulling them free of the barrel. The piston can be removed from the front of the cylinder inside the upper handguard.

6) The bolt assembly is best left together. However, the firing pin can be removed by drifting its pin out (from left to right); this also frees the extractor

The release for the trigger group is located at the rear of the trigger guard (the rounded triangle with a small detent in its center). Often a punch and rubber mallet are needed to free the catch.

The trigger group is easily cleaned and lubricated once it has been removed from the rifle during field stripping.

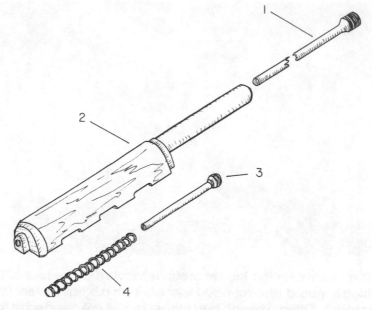

Gas Tube Assembly: (1) piston, (2) handguard/gas cylinder, (3) piston extension, and (4) piston extension return spring.

The gas assembly release lever is located on the right side of the block holding the rear sight. The lever is rotated upward to free the handguard/gas tube.

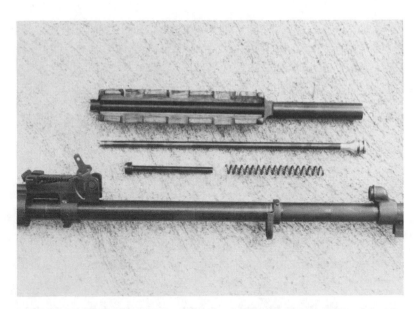

Field stripped gas tube assembly. Note the spring that makes the gas piston extension (that is inside the block holding the rear sight) hard to replace and can propel it out of the rifle if it isn't restrained during field stripping

and its spring so care must be taken not to lose them since the spring is under pressure.

7) The recoil spring and its guide can be disassembled by retracting the spring backward and then pulling the spring retainer off the rod and freeing it. This will allow the spring to be eased forward and freed.

Detail Stripping of the SKS

The trigger group should not normally be disassembled and when such work is done, it is best left to a gunsmith.

For those capable of such work, disassembly is not overly complex. First, the safety should be released and the hammer eased forward by releasing it with the trigger after depressing the

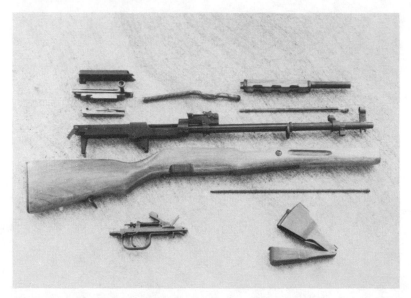

The completely field stripped SKS. The user has complete access to all the parts so cleaning and oiling can be carried out efficiently.

disconnector at the front of the trigger group slightly so the trigger connects with the sear (if the disconnector is depressed too much, the hammer will not be freed by the trigger). Once lowered, the hammer can then be levered back against its spring (cautiously since it's under spring pressure) and removed out the back of the openings in the trigger group housing (the hammer is held in place only by the spring pressure of the large spring and the hammer strut behind it). Drifting out the pin of the hammer strut will release it from the hammer.

Drifting out the large cross pin at the front of the trigger group will release the magazine catch, its spring, and the sear (care must be exercised since this spring is also under pressure). All the other parts of the trigger group can be removed by drifting

Trigger group: (35) cover latch, (36) latch spring/sear spring, (37) sear, (38) latch stop pin, (39), disconnector hinge pin, (41) trigger pin, (42) safety catch, (43) safety catch spring, (44) trigger, (45) safety catch pin, (46) trigger bar, (47) trigger bar pin, (48) trigger spring, (49) disconnector, (50) rebound disconnector, (51) hammer, (52) hammer strut pin, (53) hammer strut, and (54) hammer spring.

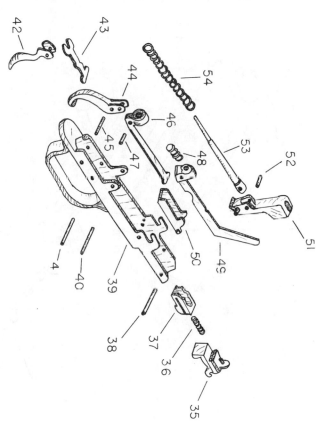

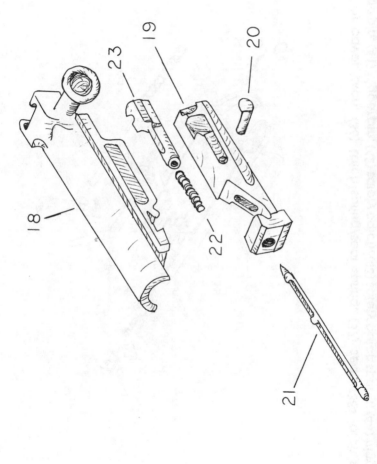

Bolt assembly: (18) Bolt carrier, (19) bolt, (20) firing pin retainer, (21) firing pin, (22) extractor spring, and (23) extractor.

out the remaining cross pins. The bolt can be disassembled by drifting out its firing pin retainer which will free the firing pin and the extractor and its spring. Since the extractor is spring loaded, care must be taken to restrain it.

Reassembly of the SKS

Reassembly of the SKS is basically a reversal of the above procedures. After field stripping, usually getting the gas piston extension and its spring back into the space under the rear sight is a headache. However, if a little care is taken the two can be trapped with the release lever and then the handguard, gas tube, and piston carefully positioned to hold the two troublesome parts as the parts are reassembled while the release lever is locked. (Once this is done, the shooter should sit down, put his feet up, and take a rest after a job well done.)

Great care is needed if the firing pin has been removed; it can be inserted into the bolt upside down during reassembly. When properly reassembled, a small milled section in the pin will allow the cross pin retaining it to be easily pushed through the hole in the bolt; if the pin is upside down, forcing the cross pin through the hole will bend the firing pin and lock it in place. The rifle can then be reassembled, creating a dangerous situation since a slam fire will occur when a round is chambered, perhaps leading to uncontrolled automatic fire if more cartridges are in the magazine.

Except for these design features, reassembly is not too difficult, though as mentioned earlier, the trigger guard will sometimes need to be "helped" with a gentle tap from a rubber mallet.

Cleaning

As with any other firearms, proper maintenance will extend the useful life of the SKS and it more reliably. Abuse or careless cleaning techniques of can quickly spoil or even ruin the rifle.

Anyone getting ready to clean a firearm should be sure it's unloaded; more than a few people have been injured by "unloaded" firearms. That said, the main consideration in cleaning is to avoid damage to the muzzle. The reason for this, it is the last part of the barrel to touch a bullet as it leaves the gun; any nick or flaw in the muzzle will send a bullet on its way with an extra wobble in flight or allow gas to jet past the bullet and propel it to one side ever so slightly.

A muzzle brake or flash hider mounted on a rifle will help protect the muzzle when the gun is being used in the field (these are discussed in chapter 4). Cleaning the barrel from the receiver end of the gun or being very careful not to rub the cleaning rod against the sides of the bore if cleaning from the muzzle end of the barrel will help prevent damaging the muzzle.

The idea when shoving cleaning patches and the brush through the barrel is to maneuver dirt from the chamber to the muzzle (or, if cleaning from the muzzle end, from the muzzle to the chamber). This can't be achieved by stroking the patches or brush back and forth since this just shoves the fouling up and down the bore without getting it out of the barrel. Instead the brush and patches should be shoved through the bore and then removed before drawing the cleaning rod back.

The cleaning rod that comes with the SKS will work fine for the job (shooters should check it by rolling it on a flat surface to be sure it isn't bent). The cleaning kit that comes with most of these rifles will complete the tools needed for cleaning (for those with rifles that didn't come with a cleaning kit, these can be purchased for just $6 from Gun Parts or Navy Arms). Some old strips of cloth or patches (available at gun stores) and solvents/lubricants designed for such tasks will make quick work of cleaning chores.

Bore cleaning should be started with a brush soaked in a solvent on the cleaning rod. The best

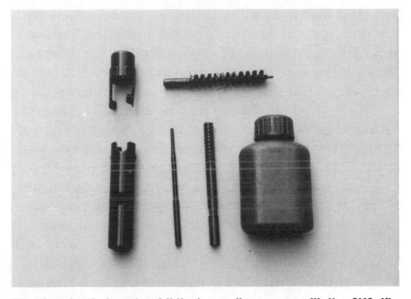

The standard cleaning kit that usually comes with the SKS rifle is excellent for maintaining the rifle. Shown here is the Chinese-made kit offered by *Navy Arms*.

solvent for this purpose is one of the new solvent/ lubricants that makes cleaning more of a one-step operation than it is with a separate solvent followed by the application of oil. Among the best of these new liquids are Break-Free and Tri-Lube, both readily available at gun stores.

The solvent-soaked brush is first run through the bore (in one direction) to loosen dirt. Once the brush has been utilized, very tight, dry patches are shoved through the bore (again, in one direction). These are followed by a patch soaked in solvent, so the bore is liberally coated with the liquid. Ideally, the SKS is set aside for at least a half hour so the solvent can loosen up any fouling that remains in the bore at this point.

The next step is to run a wire brush through the bore and follow by alternating solvent-soaked and dry patches. This is continued until the patches come through clean. A dry patch is then shoved through the bore (if the gun is to be stored, it is not necessary to oil the bore since it is chrome lined).

The SKS's bolt should also be carefully cleaned, with special attention paid to the various crevices of its face. The firing pin and its hole in the bolt as well as the extractor are key parts to clean thoroughly.

Much the same process used on the bore should be used on the gas tube, especially if corrosive ammunition is ever fired in the gun. Excess oil should be carefully wiped from the piston and the tube since it can gum up with the intense heat that is generated by the hot gases coming into the gas tube.

A very light coat of lubricant on the trigger group and all exterior metal parts is wise to help prevent rust. Care must be taken not to leave heavy coats of oil in the chamber or magazine, however, since lubricants will quickly deactivate ammunition when the material seeps into it (which can happen at an alarming rate with even minor amounts of oil present in the magazine/chamber area).

In dusty environments, the exterior coat of oil should be minimized since it attracts dirt; rifles that will be stored for a while before used should have a heavy coat of oil which is wiped off when the gun is removed from storage.

After the firearm has been cleaned, the bore should be checked for patch threads, oil, or foreign materials before it is fired since anything left in the barrel can ruin it when the firearm is discharged.

Storage

An SKS should never be stored in a leather or air-tight plastic storage case. Leather generally attracts moisture and often contains acids which will attack the metal of the gun with time; many plastic containers allow moisture to condense inside them which promotes rust.

"Gun socks" for storing the SKS are ideal for protecting the rifle without having excessive rust problems. These are available from L.L. Baston and other companies for less than $10 each.

For long-term storage, Outers offers several types of thick lubricants and rust preventives; these are available at most large gun stores.

Touch Up of the SKS's Finish

It's simple to touch up the metal finish of an SKS to hide minor scratches as well as wear along the edges of the gun. The secret to darkening steel parts is to apply some touch up blue to these areas. This liquid is available in most gun stores as well as from Brownell's.

Minor rust spots can also be removed from the SKS with fine steel wool soaked in oil. Once the surface is free of rust, the "white" steel can be refinished with touch up blue after first removing the oil with acetone or alcohol.

For best results, the instructions on the touch up blue container should be followed carefully and the steel surface worked on should be carefully cleaned and oiled after being darkened with this chemical.

Refinishing Wooden Stocks

Since the stocks on most SKS rifles look like they've gone through a war—and on the losing side at that—refinishing them is generally unnecessary, especially on "knock about" guns that are often tossed into the truck without a suitable case or slammed into a rack in the back of a pickup truck. Often these stocks are in such poor shape that they should be retired (perhaps even buried) and replaced with an aftermarket stock (covered in the preceeding chapter).

However, if shooters want to try their hand at refinishing a stock, the steps are fairly simple if somewhat time consuming. The materials are fairly simple with finish remover, varnish, and finishing oil all readily available from outlets like Brownell's or even local paint stores. Brushes, steel wool (coarse and fine), and sandpaper will round out the needed equipment.

First, all metal parts are removed from the stock and the original finish is stripped from the wood which is then allowed to dry. After the moisture has evaporated from the stock, sanding, reshaping, and filling of holes as needed is carried out. Often some cautious reshaping will make the military stock of the SKS much more suitable for the shooter's needs;

this is carried out at this point in the operation.

Deep dents can sometimes be popped out of a wooden stock by placing a damp cloth over the area and laying a hot clothes iron over the spot. This may need to be repeated several times before the dent comes out. And some dents won't come out if they're too deep or the wood has been crushed or cut. Then wood filler, Plastic Wood, or colored epoxy will be needed to fill the dent, matching the surrounding wood as closely as possible. Scraping the wood with a sharp blade will also help the final finish and can smooth out minor dings and scratches. Sanding with medium and then fine sandpaper will finish this step.

For the very best finish, it's usually necessary to do some wet-and-dry sanding, wetting the wood between sandings and applying heat to the wood (with a heat gun or gas flame) to raise the grain. This process is continued until the grain no longer rises with each steaming. At this point it is possible to add checking to the stock or even stain it to suit the shooters taste. (Checkering is an art unto itself. Checkering tools along with instructions on using them are also available from Brownell's.)

At this point, the stock is allowed to dry and then covered with an undercoat of thinned varnish, coating the stock inside and out in order to seal the wood against moisture should it and its owner get caught in the outdoors during inclement weather.

Several days of drying is allowed before the stock is again lightly sanded leaving a smoothing coating of varnish on the exterior of the wood. For best results, linseed oil is applied according to the directions given for treating gun stocks. For those wanting a shiny finish, the stock can be waxed with furniture wax or a similar product, but many shooters will prefer to leave it dull so it won't reflect light to attract unwanted attention.

●●●●●●

With proper care the SKS can give its owner more than a lifetime of service and still be capable of being passed on to several more generations of shooters to boot. The SKS may not be a pretty gun, but it is built to last not for decades but centuries.

Given the low price tags these guns carry, that's an amazing piece of engineering!

Appendix

Manufacturers of Accessories and Ammo
Books of Interest

Action Arms
P. O. Box 9573
Philadelphia, PA 19124
Scopes suitable for the SKS

Adventurer's Outpost
P. O. Box 70
Cottonwood, AZ 86326
Accessories including tactical lights

Aimpoint, USA
580 Herndon Parkway, Suite 500
Herndon, VA 22070
Manufacturer of electric dot scopes and lasers

B-Square Company
Box 11281
Ft. Worth, TX 76110
Scope mounts, lasers, tools, and bipods

Beeman Precision Firearms
47 Paul Dr.San Rafael, CA 94903
Distributor of scopes and other
firearm accessories

Brigade Quartermasters
1025 Cobb International Blvd.
Kennesaw, GA 30144-4349
Web gear, shooting glasses, and other supplies
and accessories useful to owners of the SKS

Brownells, Inc.
Rt. 2, Box 1
Montezuma, IA 50171
Gunsmithing tools, gun accessories, and related
products

Century International Arms
48 Lower Newton St.
St. Albans, VT 05478
Importer of SKS rifles and accessories

Cherokee Gun Accessories
4127 Bay St., Suite 226
Fremont, CA 94538
Stainless steel folding bipod for rifles

Choate Machine & Tool
Box 218
Bald Knob, AR 72010
 Accessories including SKS stock

Cobray
P.O. Box 813218
Smyrna, GA 30081
Flare launcher attachment for SKS rifles

Combat Exchange
P.O. Box 1596
Burgaw, NC 28425
Plastic stocks for SKS

COMPASSECO, Inc.
P.O. Box 427, 801 Taylorsville Rd.
Bloomfield, KY 40008
TS45 Chinese-made air rifle modeled off the
SKS rifle

Concorde Arms, Inc.
27820 Fremont Ct., Unit 3
Valencia, CA 91355
Military surplus parts and accessories for the
SKS

Delta Press
Box 1625
El Dorado, AR 71730
Publisher of military manuals, gun books, and
related products

E&L Manufacturing, Inc.
39042 N. Schoolhouse Rd.
Cave Creek, AZ 85331
SKS buttstock extensions, etc.

Federal Arms, Inc.
1602 Selby Ave.
St. Paul, MN 55104
Birch and Walnut thumbhole stocks for the SKS

Firearms Specialties Manufacturing
RD 1, Box 354
Neshanic Station, NJ 08853
"SKS-47" pistol grip stock for SKS rifle

Golden Key Futura
14090-6100 Rd., P.O. Box 1446
Montrose, CO 81401
30-round fixed box conversion magazine for SKS
rifle

Gun Parts Corporation
West Hurley, NY 12491
SKS Stowaway Pistol Grip, SKS Flash Hider,
and Muzzlebrake

Guns (Div. of DC Engineering, Inc.)
8633 Southfield
Detroit, MI 48228
37-round detachable box magazine conversion
for SKS rifle

Harris Engineering, Inc.
Barlow, Kentucky 42024
Bipods

Hellfire Systems, Inc.
P.O. Box 549
Olathe, CO 81425
Trigger-lever assembly for legal "auto" fire of the
SKS

Hesco Inc.
2821 Greenville Rd.
La Grange, GA 30240
U. S. distributor of Meprolight tritium night sights

K-Loc Mounts, Inc.
6531 W. 56th Ave., #31
Arvada, CO 80002
Scope mounts, magazines, and magazine spacers
for SKS rifle

L. L. Baston Company
P. O. Box 1995
El Dorado, AR 71730
Dealer in accessories suitable for use with the
SKS

Michaels of Oregon Company
P. O. Box 13010
Portland, OR 97213
Rifle slings, ammunition pouches, etc.

Midwest Ordnance, Inc.
18315 Weaver
Detroit, MI 48228
Custom modifications to SKS rifle to accommodate 30-round magazines, drum magazines, fold
ing stocks, etc. (before BATF ban on many of
these modifications)

Navy Arms Company
689 Bergen Blvd.
Ridgefield, NJ 076057
Importer of SKS rifles and accessories

Ram-Line
10601 West 48th Ave.
Wheat Ridge, CO 80401
Manufacturer of bipods and other accessories

SARCO, Inc.
323 Union St.
Stirling, NJ 07980
Military surplus equipment, magazines, gun
parts, accessories, etc.

S&K Manufacturing Company
Box 247
Pittsfield, PA 16340   Scope mounts for the SKS

Shotgun News
P.O. Box 669
Hastings, NE 68902
"Newspaper" of advertisements by various fire
arms manufacturers and accessory supplies.

SOS, Inc.
130 E. Main #285
Medford, OR 97501
30-round box magazine for SKS

Tapco
P.O. Box 575
Powder Springs, GA 30073
20-round SKS magazines, replacement stocks,
and scope mounts

Tasco
3625 NW 82nd Ave., Suite 310
Miami, FL 33166
Scopes suitable for use on the SKS

U.S. AMMUNITION
IMPORTERS/MANUFACTURERS

Action Ammo, Ltd.
P. O. Box 19630
Philadelphia, PA 19124

Black Hills Ammunition
P.O. Box 5070
Rapid City, SD 57709

Federal Cartridge Company
900 Ehlen Dr.
Anoka, MN 55303

Hornady Manufacturing Co.
P.O. Box 1848
Grand Island, NE 68802

Olin/Winchester
120 Long Ridge Rd.
Stamford, CT 06904

PMC—Eldorado Cartridge
P. O. Box 308
Boulder City, NV 89005

SELECTED FIREARMS BOOKS
OF INTEREST TO OWNERS OF THE SKS

AK47: THE COMPLETE KALASHNIKOV FAMILY OF ASSAULT RIFLES
By Duncan Long
Delta Press, Ltd.
P. O. Box 1625
El Dorado, AR 71731-1625

THE AK47 STORY
By Edward Clinton Ezell
Stackpole Books
Cameron and Kelker Streets, P. O. Box 1831
Harrisburg, PA 17105

ASSAULT PISTOLS, RIFLES AND SUBMACHINE GUNS
By Duncan Long
Delta Press, Ltd.
P. O. Box 1625
El Dorado, AR 71731-1625

MILITARY SMALL ARMS
By Ian V. Hogg and John Weeks
DBI Books, Inc.
One Northfield Plaza
Northfield, IL 60093

SMALL ARMS TODAY
By Edward Clinton Ezell
Stackpole Books
Cameron and Kelker Streets
P. O. Box 1831
Harrisburg, PA 17105

SMALL ARMS OF THE WORLD
By Edward Clinton Ezell
Stackpole Books
Cameron and Kelker Streets
 P. O. Box 1831
Harrisburg, PA 17105

Notes

Notes

Notes

Other Books Available From Desert Publications

PRICES SUBJECT TO CHANGE WITHOUT NOTICE **Desert Publications**

800-852-4445

215 S. Washington Dept. -BK-065
El Dorado, AR 71730 USA

Shipping & handling
1 item $5.95 - 2 or more $9.95